INDIANS

BLACK HAWK, *Cleven*
OSCEOLA, *Clark*
POCAHONTAS, *Seymour*
PONTIAC, *Peckham*
SACAGAWEA, *Seymour*
SEQUOYAH, *Snow*
SITTING BULL, *Stevenson*
SQUANTO, *Stevenson*
TECUMSEH, *Stevenson*

NAVAL HEROES

DAVID FARRAGUT, *Long*
GEORGE DEWEY, *Long*
JOHN PAUL JONES, *Snow*
MATTHEW CALBRAITH PERRY, *Scharbach*
OLIVER HAZARD PERRY, *Long*
RAPHAEL SEMMES, *Snow*
STEPHEN DECATUR, *Smith*

NOTED WIVES and MOTHERS

ABIGAIL ADAMS, *Wagoner*
DOLLY MADISON, *Monsell*
ELEANOR ROOSEVELT, *Weil*
JESSIE FREMONT, *Wagoner*
MARTHA WASHINGTON, *Wagoner*
MARY TODD LINCOLN, *Wilkie*
NANCY HANKS, *Stevenson*
RACHEL JACKSON, *Govan*

SCIENTISTS and INVENTORS

ABNER DOUBLEDAY, *Dunham*
ALBERT EINSTEIN, *Hammontree*
ALECK BELL, *Widdemer*
CYRUS MCCORMICK, *Dobler*
ELI WHITNEY, *Snow*
ELIAS HOWE, *Corcoran*
ELIZABETH BLACKWELL, *Henry*
GAIL BORDEN, *Paradis*
GEORGE CARVER, *Stevenson*
GEORGE EASTMAN, *Henry*
GEORGE PULLMAN, *Myers*
GEORGE WESTINGHOUSE, *Dunham*
HENRY FORD, *Aird and Ruddiman*
JOHN AUDUBON, *Mason*
JOHN BURROUGHS, *Frisbee*
JOHN DEERE, *Bare*
JOHN FITCH, *Stevenson*
LEE DEFOREST, *Dobler*
LUTHER BURBANK, *Burt*
MARIA MITCHELL, *Melin*
ROBERT FULTON, *Henry*
ROBERT GODDARD, *Moore*

S...
T...
W...
WILL...
Stevenson
WILL AND CHARLIE MAYO, *Hammontree*

SOCIAL and CIVIC LEADERS

BETSY...
BOOK...
CLAR...
DAN...
DORO...
FRAN...
J. STE...
JANE...
JOHN...
JULIA...
JULIE...
LILIU...
LUCR...
MOLL...
OLIVE...
SUSAN...

SOL...

ANTHO...
BEDFO...
DAN...
DOUG...
ETHAN...
FRANC...
GEORG...
ISRAEL...
JEB ST...
NATH...
ROBE...
SAM H...
TOM J...
U. S. G...
WILLI...
ZACK...

STATESMEN

ABE LINCOLN, *Stevenson*
ANDY JACKSON, *Stevenson*
DAN WEBSTER, *Smith*
FRANKLIN ROOSEVELT, *Weil*
HENRY CLAY, *Monsell*
HERBERT HOOVER, *Comfort*
JAMES MONROE, *Widdemer*
JEFF DAVIS, *de Grummond and Delaune*
JOHN F. KENNEDY, *Frisbee*
JOHN MARSHALL, *Monsell*
TEDDY ROOSEVELT, *Parks*
WOODROW WILSON, *Monsell*

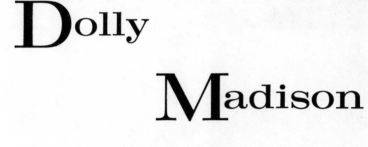

Dolly Madison

Quaker Girl

Illustrated by Gray Morrow

Dolly Madison

Quaker Girl

by Helen Albee Monsell

 THE **BOBBS-MERRILL** COMPANY, INC.
A SUBSIDIARY OF HOWARD W. SAMS & CO., INC.
Publishers • INDIANAPOLIS • NEW YORK

LIBRARY OF CONGRESS CATALOG CARD NUMBER: 60-7715

PRINTED IN THE UNITED STATES OF AMERICA

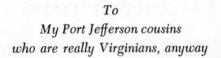

To
My Port Jefferson cousins
who are really Virginians, anyway

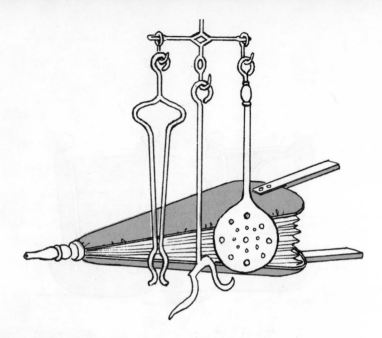

Illustrations

Numerous smaller illustrations

Contents

Books by Helen Albee Monsell

DOLLY MADISON: QUAKER GIRL

HENRY CLAY: MILL BOY OF THE SLASHES

JOHN MARSHALL: BOY OF YOUNG AMERICA

ROBERT E. LEE: BOY OF OLD VIRGINIA

SUSAN ANTHONY: GIRL WHO DARED

TOM JACKSON: YOUNG STONEWALL

TOM JEFFERSON: A BOY IN COLONIAL DAYS

WOODROW WILSON: BOY PRESIDENT

★ **Dolly Madison**

Madison

Quaker Girl

A Baby Comes Home

IT WAS a late summer day in 1768. Two little boys were sitting on the fence in front of their home in Hanover County, Virginia. Walter was old enough to wear trousers. Temple was young enough to wear skirts. He wasn't even old enough to talk plainly yet.

Both boys had on their very best clothes. Even their hands were spic-and-span clean. Mammy Amy had just scrubbed both of them.

"And she said we mustn't get ourselves mussed up," Walter complained. "She wants us to look like 'little gentlemen' when Mother and Father get here."

You couldn't have much fun if you had to keep your clothes looking like a "little gentleman's" all the time. You couldn't go down to the tobacco field with the men. You couldn't slide down haystacks.

"Let's go sit on the fence," Walter had said. "We can look down the road and watch for the coach to come."

So now they were perched on the fence. They looked like two fat little robins.

There was nothing coming down the road.

"I wish the coach would come *quick*," said Walter. "Mother and Father have been gone a long time."

Mother and Father had been visiting down in North Carolina. Now they were coming home.

"I wonder if they will bring us any presents," said Walter. "Maybe they will bring me a knife. I am old enough to have a good one, now."

"I want a knife, too," said Temple.

"Look!" cried Walter. "Somebody is coming down the road now."

Temple leaned over so far he nearly tumbled down. But Walter pulled him back.

"There isn't enough dust for a carriage. It is just somebody on horseback."

Sure enough—down the road came an old man on a white horse. He had a big bag of corn across the horse's back. The white horse was old, too. He didn't move fast enough to raise much dust.

"It's old Zeke," said Walter. "He's probably on the way to the mill. He is going to have his corn ground into corn meal.

"Howdy, Zeke."

"Howdy," said the old man.

The white horse stopped. It always stopped whenever it had a chance.

Old Zeke looked at the boys. He screwed up his eyes.

"You sure are dressed up mighty fine."

"Mother and Father are coming home today," said Walter.

"They'll bring us a present," said Temple.

"You don't say!"

Then old Zeke began to chuckle. "My old woman tells me they are bringing you one present that you've never had before."

"Not *either* of us?"

"Not either of you."

"What is it, Zeke?"

"Just you wait and see."

He switched at the old white horse. "I got to be getting along."

BETTER THAN A KNIFE

The children waited a long time. At last they saw another cloud of dust down the road.

"It *must* be the coach this time," cried Walter.

And it was.

14

The boys jumped down from the fence. They ran to open the big gate.

The road was a clay road. It was covered with thick red dust. Two little boys could certainly kick up a lot of dust when they ran. They forgot about their clean clothes. They forgot about their clean faces and hands. And now they weren't clean any more.

But Mother wouldn't mind. She'd be so glad to see her children again she wouldn't even notice. Besides, she had been riding a good many miles. The coach was covered with red dust, too. And Mother would have plenty of dust on herself.

The gate was a heavy gate. It had five long bars. The boys tugged it open and the horses and the coach went through. They fastened the gate again. Then they raced after the coach.

It stopped in front of the house. Mammy Amy came hurrying out.

The coachman climbed down from the box.

He opened the coach door. Then he pulled down the steps so that Father could get out.

Father turned. The boys thought he was going to help Mother down from the coach. Instead, he held out both arms. That was strange!

Mother put a bundle in his arms. It was long and soft-looking.

"It's the present," said Walter. "It's the something we've never had before."

Father held it very carefully in his arms. He turned to the boys.

"See," he said, "we've brought you a new little baby sister."

Walter didn't say a word, but it was plain to see that he would much rather have had a knife.

Just then, though, the baby opened her big blue eyes. She looked at her brothers and smiled and cooed.

"Let me take her," said Mammy Amy. "Come to your old mammy, honey."

She was a very little baby, but her dress was very long. So were her petticoats. They hung over Mammy's arm.

"She's a precious little lamb," said Mammy.

The baby waved her arms.

"Look," said Walter. "She's waving to us."

She gurgled again. Her brothers were pleased and interested.

"Maybe," said Walter, "it won't be such a bad idea to have a little sister, after all. What's her name, Father?"

"Dorothea."

"That's a mighty long name."

"It is, for a fact," said Father. "Like her dress. Let's call her Dolly."

An Adventurer

LITTLE DOLLY PAYNE liked her new home. Of course, she hadn't seen much of it, except Mother's room. But there were plenty of interesting things in Mother's room.

There were the red flames that danced in the fireplace. There was a big wheel in one corner. It hummed when Mammy Amy turned it. There were shiny things on top of the big chest of drawers. Dolly wanted to play with all of them.

At first she just lay in her cradle. She would wave her little arms and try to kick up her feet. It was hard to kick under those long skirts.

Finally she grew big enough to crawl. But a

baby just *couldn't* crawl in long skirts. Mother had to cut them down. Even then they came to her ankles. They certainly kept her knees from getting scratched. But how she could get over the floor!

By the time Aunt Dorothea came to visit, little Dolly had learned to walk, too. She had learned to do something else, but nobody had found out about that yet.

Grown-up people were queer. And brothers were just as bad. Whenever she tried to do anything while they were watching, they said, "No, no, Dolly."

When she tried to catch the pretty fire, they said, "No, no. Baby will get burned."

When she tried to find out what made the big wheel turn, they said, "No, no. Baby mustn't touch that."

But they couldn't say "No, no," to her new trick because they didn't know what it was.

The boys didn't stay around the house much when company came. It was more fun to go down to the barn to play, or to run and jump out in the fields.

But Aunt Dorothea was different from most company. She was jolly, and she liked boys. They were glad Baby Dolly had been named for a nice person like Aunt Dorothea.

She didn't have to be treated like company. She came right into Mother's room like home folks. She picked Baby Dolly up and tossed her in the air. Dolly laughed and crowed.

Then she put the baby down on the floor to play. She took her sewing from her bag and said, "I am making my namesake a cap."

The rooms were cold. There were drafts, too, all over the house. The baby wore a cap nearly all the time.

But little Dolly wasn't interested in her new

21

cap. She could walk now, but when she wanted to get somewhere fast, she still crawled. Now she began to crawl toward the fire.

"No, no," cried her brothers. "Come back."

"She's a regular little monkey," said Aunt Dorothea.

"That she is," said Mother.

"What's a monkey?" asked Temple.

"It's a funny little animal that can crawl or climb almost anywhere."

"Has thee ever seen one?"

Aunt Dorothea shook her head. "They don't live in this country."

"Didn't thy grandfather see one when he crossed the mountain?"

"Goodness, no! He saw plenty of other strange beasts, though—bears and wolves and panthers."

"Tell us about it," begged Walter.

Mammy was busy at the spinning wheel. Mother was teaching one of the house servants to sew. None of them stopped working, but they all looked pleased. They liked to hear Aunt Dorothea's stories.

GRANDFATHER SPOTSWOOD'S ADVENTURE

"My grandfather," said Aunt Dorothea, "was Governor Spotswood. He lived in the Governor's Palace in Williamsburg. The land is very flat down there, but the Indians were always telling about the mountains back toward the West. Grandfather Spotswood wanted to see those mountains himself.

"At last, he invited some of his friends to go with him. They would do what very few white men had ever done before. They would climb the Blue Mountains.

"The ground around Williamsburg was soft and sandy. The horses there didn't need iron horseshoes to protect their feet. Grandfather knew the mountains would be rocky. He had the blacksmith make iron shoes for the horses before they started.

"For more than a month they rode toward the mountains. There were no roads. There weren't even any paths. They had to keep riding along the riverbank.

"At first the land was flat. Then there were hills. Finally, away off, they saw something blue against the sky. At first they thought it was thick blue clouds."

"But it wasn't!" cried Walter. "It was the Blue Mountains!"

"It was. And climbing those mountains, let me tell you, was hard work. The horses never had tried anything like that before. Neither had the men. Sometimes the way was so steep they had to get down and lead the horses. The trees were so thick they couldn't see ahead of them. They couldn't see behind them. There might be

Indians hiding behind those trees. Or there could be bears!

"But they kept on. Finally it grew lighter. Then they came out of the woods. There was a good stiff breeze blowing. They were on top of the mountain. They could see for miles and miles on the other side."

"I bet they cheered!" cried Walter.

"I wager they did, too. They drank a toast to King George, and then——"

Crash!

Everybody jumped. They had been too much interested in Aunt Dorothea's story to keep an eye on Dolly.

Dolly was like Governor Spotswood. She liked to explore, too. And the new thing she had learned to do was to climb.

She had climbed from the floor onto a chair. From the chair she had climbed to Mother's desk. Then, from the desk she had climbed up on the

chest of drawers. She had reached for one of the
shiny candlesticks.

The big brass candlestick was heavy. When
she dropped it, it fell on the fingers of her other
hand. Then it rolled from the chest of drawers
and fell down to the floor.

Crash!

Dolly began to scream.

26

"Will you just look at that baby!" cried Aunt Dorothea.

Mammy rushed over to the chest of drawers. She lifted down the screaming Dolly.

"Give her to me," said Aunt Dorothea.

She cuddled the little girl in her lap.

"There, there!" said Aunt Dorothea.

Dolly liked to be cuddled. She stopped crying at once.

THE KNIGHTS OF THE GOLDEN HORSESHOE

"Go on with the story," begged Walter.

"There is not much else to tell. They climbed down the mountainside into the valley. We call it the Shenandoah Valley now.

"After they had rested for a while, they started back. Of course they had to climb the mountain again, but it was easier this time. They knew where they were going."

"It's always easier going home," said Walter.

"When they got back to Williamsburg, Grandfather gave each of the men who had gone with him a little golden horseshoe. It had jewels that looked like horseshoe nails. And he promised one just like it to every man who would cross the Blue Mountains. They would be the 'Knights of the Golden Horseshoe.'"

"Dolly was trying to explore, too," said Walter. "But she can't have a golden horseshoe, because we're Quakers, and Quakers can't have any jewelry."

"She's got a bruise, instead," said Temple. "There is a blue spot on her thumb, where the candlestick hit her."

Aunt Dorothea cuddled the baby in her lap. "Oh, well—explorers generally do get bruises. But they think it is worth it."

A Busy Day

AUNT DOROTHEA wasn't the only one who could tell good stories. Mother could, too. However, Mother was a very busy woman.

It was true that she had plenty of servants. There was Mammy Amy, the nurse. There was Mandy, the cook. There were the girls who worked in the loom room. There were the maids who did the cleaning and dusting. It did seem as though Mother ought not to have very much left to do, but she did.

"Tell me a story," said Dolly. She was four years old now. She liked stories.

It was right after breakfast. Father had gone

29

out to the tobacco fields. The boys were outdoors playing. It seemed to be a fine time for
Mother to tell her a story.

"Not yet," said Mother. "I must get Mandy
the things she needs, first."

She picked up her basket of keys.

"Let me carry them," begged Dolly.

Mother let her carry the key basket. They
went to the storeroom.

Mother opened the flour barrel. She measured
out a big bowl of flour. She measured out a big
bowl of corn meal. She brought out the salt and
the sugar and all the other things Mandy would
need to cook dinner.

Then they went to the smokehouse. Mother
gave Mandy the ham and bacon for the day.
Mandy went back to the kitchen. Now she had
everything she needed. She could go on with her
cooking for that day.

"Now tell me a story," said Dolly.

"Not yet. Next I must get the girls started on their work," Mother replied.

They went to the big back room where the loom was set up. It took a lot of cloth to keep a family like Mother's warm and comfortable. There must always be one or two girls busy with the spinning and the weaving. There must always be somebody sewing, too. Mother had to show them all what to do today.

"Now tell me a story," begged Dolly.

"Not yet. Mandy knows how to cook the meat and the vegetables, but I must go make the pies and cakes for dinner."

They went back to the kitchen. There was no better kitchen in all Hanover County. There was a big fireplace. It had a brick oven on one side. There were big hooks to hang kettles on, over the blaze. There were iron kettles, so big that Dolly could almost climb inside of them and play house.

While Mother was making her pies a little

Negro girl came to the door. She said, "Ma's got a bad misery in her head this morning. And Sam cut his leg with the ax yesterday when he was chopping wood."

"All right," said Mother. "I'll come and see them right away."

Dolly knew there could be no story until after the sick folks had been taken care of.

When anybody on the plantation was very ill, they sent for the doctor. But he lived miles away. When folks had just ordinary aches and pains, Mother was the doctor.

She and Dolly got their sunbonnets. They put some medicines and some bandages in a basket. They went down to the little houses where the servants lived, back of the Big House.

Mother talked with the woman who had a misery in her head. She gave her some medicine.

She washed the cut on Sam's leg. She put on ointment and wrapped it in clean bandages.

Then they started back to the house.

"Now tell me a story," said Dolly.

"Not quite yet," said Mother. "I must take care of the books for thy father."

Everything that was bought for the farm had to be put down in a big book. Everything that was made on the farm and everything that was sold had to be put down too. Mother kept all the records in these books.

They went back to Mother's room. Dolly was too big for the cradle now, but there was a new baby there. Mother stopped to play with her for a minute. Then she went over to her desk. She began to work on the books.

Dolly knew she must keep quiet while Mother was writing. She sat down on the floor by the fireplace. She leaned her back against the stool. Following Mother was enough to tire anybody.

"There!" said Mother. She put down her pen. She pushed back her books.

She picked up her workbasket and sat down in her chair by the fireplace. There was always plenty of fine sewing for Mother to do. She began to work on the sleeve of a shirt for Father.

The baby was fretting a little. Mother put her foot on one of the cradle rockers. Her hands were busy, but she could rock the cradle with her foot.

"Now," said Mother, "I can tell thee a story."

Her daughter didn't say a word. Mother looked down. Dolly was fast asleep.

Three R's and a Sampler

SOMETHING VERY exciting happened to Temple when Dolly was four years old. Mother made him his first trousers. He was very proud that he was big enough to have real boy clothes.

Temple was very sure he looked just like Father when he put on his new suit. And he did. The coat was like Father's. So were the trousers. Mother brushed back his hair, and tied it in a club at his neck, just the way Father did.

"I declare to goodness," said Mammy Amy, "he sure does look like a man now!"

Temple ran down to the kitchen to show his new clothes to Mandy. He went to the loom room, so that the girls there could see. Then he ran down to the fields to show himself off to the men. Dolly ran along with him.

"I'm old enough now to wear trousers," said Temple. "I'm old enough to start school, too."

"I'm almost old enough to start school now, too," said Dolly.

Temple shook his head. "Girls don't start school as soon as boys do."

"Why not?"

"Because they don't have to learn as much as boys do. They don't have to learn Latin. They don't have to learn Greek. They don't have to learn anything much at all except how to read and write."

"Won't I even have to learn how to do sums?" asked Dolly.

She had watched Walter doing his sums. It looked hard. It would be nice not to have to do hard things like that.

"Well, yes," said Temple. "Thee'll have to learn to do sums."

"Why?"

"Because when thee gets married thee'll want to keep thy husband's books the same way Mother does for Father."

"Oh," said Dolly.

"But thee won't have to learn Latin. Thee won't study any of the *hard* things we boys have to study."

"Oh," said Dolly again.

All the same, when he started to school, Dolly wished she were going, too.

Temple and Walter started down the lane. Mother and Dolly stood at the door to wave.

"I'd like to go to school too," said Dolly.

"Someday," said Mother.

"Why can't I go now? Why can't I learn everything that boys learn?"

"Because girls don't need to know the same

things boys know. Besides, thee won't have time. Thee must learn things that boys will never have to learn."

Dolly liked that. It would be fun to learn something that Temple would never learn.

"When can I start?"

"Right now. Thee is four years old. That is plenty big enough to begin on one of the most important things."

"Does Walter know how to do it?"

"Not even Father knows how to do it."

"Oh! Let's begin right away."

They went back into the house. They went into Mother's room. Mother sat down by the baby's cradle.

"Bring thy stool over here," she said.

Dolly brought her stool over by Mother. The stool didn't have any back. Little girls must always sit so straight they wouldn't touch a chair back if they had one. Women sat straight, too.

Why, not even Grandmother would think of leaning back in a chair!

Mother threaded a needle. She turned a hem in a long strip of goods.

"Boys must study Latin," said Mother. "Boys must study Greek. They must do their sums. But they never learn how to sew."

She reached down in her workbasket.

"Here is the thimble I had when I was a little girl. Now it will be thy thimble. Put thy needle in the goods like this. Press it with the thimble, so. Now, let us see what little, *little* stitches thee can make."

Dolly pressed the needle with her thimble. She tried to push it through the hem. Somehow, it wouldn't go the right way. It pricked her finger. And her stitches were great big, crooked things going every which way.

Mother shook her head when she saw them. "Let's take them out and try again."

40

Dolly tried again and again and again. Every morning, she sat by Mother's chair for a long time, trying to make her needle go the way Mother's did.

She had thought it would be fun to learn something the boys would never learn. Now she wasn't so sure.

"I believe," said Dolly, "I would much rather learn to read."

THE SAMPLER

When Dolly was four years old she was sure she despised sewing. When she was five she wasn't quite so sure. By the time she was six she liked it.

Then Grandmother gave her a present. It was a piece of linen. It was about ten inches wide and about twelve inches long. Also she gave her a box of bright-colored worsteds.

"A child as quick with her needle as you are is ready to start making a sampler."

Mother drew a vine with flowers all along the edges of the sampler. Dolly worked them with the bright-colored worsteds. She worked them in cross-stitch.

"Now," said Mother, "what shall we put inside the vine? Look! Most samplers start a pattern this way, dear."

Dolly looked at the pattern. "I'd like to work that," she said.

Mother showed her how to plan and work a simple design.

She worked on her sampler while the boys were at school. Sometimes she worked on it after they came home.

One day Temple found her finishing the sampler. In a lower corner were the words DOLLEY PAYNE. He said, "How does thee know how to spell thy name?"

"Mother told me," Dolly said. After she started to school, though, she spelled it without the "E."

"My goodness," said Temple. "Thee sews on that thing all day long. Has thee forgotten how thee used to want to learn to read?"

"No," said Dolly, "I haven't forgotten."

"Well, if thee'll put down that sampler, I'll teach thee thy letters."

"I know my letters," said Dolly.

"Why, Dolly Payne, thee can't know them! Thee hasn't even got a primer!"

"I know my letters all the same. I've sewed them in my sampler. It looks just like the first page of thy primer. Big *A*, little *a*, big *B*, little *b*—I've made every one of them. I know every one of them too."

Temple opened his primer. He picked up a long stick. He began to point out the letters. "What's this?" he asked.

"That is *W*. It was the longest letter."

44

"What's this?"

"*K.*"

"What's this?"

"*B.*"

"Are you sure it's not a *D* or an *R?*"

"Of course I'm sure. When thee's finished sewing a letter, thee *knows* it."

And she did know them—every one.

School and a Spanking

EVEN THOUGH she knew her letters, Dolly was still anxious to go to school.

It wasn't that she was lonesome at home, exactly. She couldn't be. There were big brothers to play with. There were little brothers to play with. There were little sisters too. That was just the trouble. There were all *big* or *little*. She wanted somebody her own age.

In Hanover County the houses were far apart. You couldn't just run next door and play with your neighbors. At school, though, there would be other seven-year-old girls. They could all play together.

46

Once Dolly and Mammy Amy walked as far as the schoolhouse. They went down the road that led past home. Then they cut through the dark pine woods. They crossed a little brook. At last they came to a field.

It had been a tobacco field once. Now it was overgrown with weeds and wild flowers. There was goldenrod there. Wild carrots were blossoming. Broomstraw waved in the breeze. And in the middle of the field was the schoolhouse.

Dolly told Temple about their walk when he came home that afternoon.

"We stayed outside a long time," she said. "We could hear you studying. You made as much fuss as the chickens when they settle down for the night."

"If we didn't, the schoolmaster would think we were lazy do-nothings."

"I certainly would like to go to school."

"Thee wouldn't after thee had tried it."

"Why not?"

"Thee'd get tired in less than no time. The desks are fastened to the walls. The big boys and girls sit on benches facing the desks. They can lean against them when the schoolmaster isn't looking their way.

"But the little children are too young for writing lessons. They sit on long benches in the middle of the room. Their feet can't reach the floor. They mustn't squirm around. If they do, the schoolmaster will come and strike their hands with his long ruler.

"I wouldn't squirm," said Dolly.

"When it is time for the Primer Class to say their lesson, the schoolmaster calls them to the front of the room. He draws a long mark on the floor by his desk. They must stand with their toes touching the mark. They must stand very straight and still. And if anyone misses his lesson, the schoolmaster uses his ruler again."

48

"I wouldn't miss my lesson," said Dolly. "I still want to go to school."

So, at last, she did go. Mother and Mammy Amy dressed her very carefully that first day.

Mother put a big sunbonnet on Dolly's head. She sewed the bonnet strings together under Dolly's chin. "There! Now it can't come off."

It was such a big sunbonnet it came way out over Dolly's face. You had to peep inside to see her blue eyes and curly black hair. But Mother was worried for fear the sun would peep inside the bonnet and start freckles on her little girl's upturned nose.

"She must use my riding mask," said Mother. "Will thee please get it for us, Mammy?"

Mammy Amy went to Mother's wardrobe. She came back with the riding mask. It was made of linen. It looked like a false face. Mother tied it on under the sunbonnet. Now Dolly's face was completely hidden.

49

"We don't want her arms to get brown either,"
said Mother.

Mammy Amy went to the wardrobe again and
came back with some long gloves.

With gloves, mask, and sunbonnet, Dolly was
ready for school. But, goodness, she was hot!

The boys had been ready for some time. Nobody worried about *their* complexions.

Mother and Mammy Amy waved to them as they went off.

"Take good care of Dolly, boys," Mother called after them.

"Yes, ma'am."

BREAD AND WATER, BEADS, AND AN INVITATION

Dolly loved bright colors and pretty hats and dresses. "Mother," she said, "why can't we have bright-colored dresses and pretty hats and beautiful jewelry?"

"Daughter," her mother replied, "it is because we're Quakers. Our religion teaches us to be plain and humble. We believe it is sinful to wear colors and ornaments. Just as it is wicked to dance and sing worldly songs."

Dolly knew her parents did not know that the slaves did those things secretly. She and Temple had seen and heard them.

One evening Dolly went to bed early. She could not sleep. She had overheard the maids and the cook talking excitedly about the fun they would have tonight.

She jumped out of bed and dressed. She forgot her cap, but picked up a shawl to keep her shoulders warm. Quickly and quietly she ran downstairs and outside. She followed the faint music coming from the slaves' quarters.

In her room on the third floor, Mammy Amy awoke. She had a feeling that something was wrong. She thought at once of her favorite "chile," Dolly. Quietly she felt her way down the stairs to Dolly's room. Dolly wasn't there! Mammy Amy was frightened. She went to Father's room and knocked on his door.

"Our little Dolly's gone," she cried. "I jes' know somethin' terrible has happened to her!"

Father dressed quickly. They went outside, wondering which way to look first. Mammy Amy kept crying and saying, "I've lost my little Dolly. It's all my fault."

Father soon heard the music at the slave quarters. He ran toward it. Mammy Amy followed as fast as she could. When he reached the cabins he stopped and stared.

A Negro was playing his fiddle. All the others sang or danced. Suddenly, in the moonlight, Dolly appeared, singing and dancing to the music with the others.

John Payne was glad that his daughter was safe. But he was very angry because she had joined the others in forbidden pleasure. He strode toward her. Dolly quickly ran toward the house. Father soon caught up with her. Right then and there he spanked her. Then he took her back to the house and locked her in her room.

Dolly sobbed until she dropped off to sleep. At breakfast time, Mammy Amy brought her bread and water.

Dolly watched out the window all day. She saw the family and servants busy doing their regular duties. She wondered how long Father would keep her locked in her room. Forever? Crying, she finally crawled into her bed and fell sound asleep.

Next morning Father came. "Daughter, has thee prayed to be forgiven?" he asked.

Dolly shook her head. She knew she must be truthful, even though it might mean another spanking for her.

Father was very angry. Before he could say any more, however, Mammy Amy came in. "Time to get my little girl dressed. Her grandmother is downstairs and wants to see her."

Dolly knew her father hadn't forgiven her. At least, though, he did not spank her again. She could leave her room. And she truly loved to visit with Grandmother!

Grandmother's carriage was in front of the

house. Grandmother's coachman was down by the springhouse, talking to Mandy.

Dolly went into Mother's room. Grandmother had Baby Mary in her lap. Mother was busy with her sewing.

Dolly dropped a curtsy to Grandmother. Mother looked up at her and smiled.

"She is a very well-mannered child," said Grandmother.

"She is a big girl now," Mother told her. "She goes to school."

Dolly didn't look happy.

"What is the matter?" asked Mother. "Isn't school like thee thought it would be?"

"It is all right, Mother. Only, why can't I dress like the other girls?"

"T'ch, t'ch," said Grandmother. She put the baby in the cradle and started knitting.

Mother looked worried. "Don't the other girls wear sunbonnets and masks?"

"Oh, yes. That part of it is all right. But they have pretty dresses with ruffles. They aren't like this ugly old gray thing."

She looked down at her own dress. It was a dull gray color, and it was very, very plain.

"Thee is a little Quaker girl," said Mother. "The Quakers do not like to see their women-folk rigged out in fancy clothes, with gaudy colors. Thee must remember what William Penn said, dear: 'If thou are but clean and warm, it is enough.'"

Dolly's dress was clean, and it was certainly warm. But she didn't agree with William Penn.

"Nancy has a bracelet. And Peg has a chain with blue beads."

Mother shook her head. "Keep thy hands busy with good works; then they will need no rings or bracelets to make them beautiful. And a kindly smile is better than the finest necklace."

"Nonsense!" said Grandmother. She wasn't a

56

Quaker. "Every girl wants pretty things. And she ought to have them.

"Suppose you let Dolly come home with me to spend the night. Her grandfather is going to the Courthouse tomorrow or next day. He can bring her back when he rides by."

"But what about school?"

"She is really too young to start school yet."

Mother wasn't sure.

"I already know more than Nancy and Peg do," said Dolly. "I know all my letters. They don't. If I don't go back until they've caught up with me, then we can all be together."

"Maybe you are right," Mother agreed.

She had hated to say no about the pretty clothes. She thought if Dolly went to visit Grandmother, she might forget about them.

"*Please*, Mother!" Dolly begged.

"Well . . . all right. Run ask Mammy Amy to get you ready."

Dolly was out of the room almost before Mother finished speaking. "Mammy Amy!" she called. "I'm going home with Grandmother."

She chattered away like a little blue jay all the while Mammy Amy was smoothing her hair. "Won't it be fun? Maybe Grandmother will let me turn the big spinning wheel. Maybe she'll teach me one or two steps in the minuet. She did the last time I was there."

Already she had forgotten about Peg's blue necklace.

"Stand still, child," said Mammy Amy. "How can I fasten your bonnet with you jumping around like a hoppergrass?"

Dolly was ready long before Grandmother.

"Does thee have thy sampler?" asked Mother. "A little girl mustn't be idle, Dolly, even when she is visiting."

"She won't be idle," said Grandmother. "We are making candles tomorrow."

58

To Work or Play?

DRIVING HOME with Grandmother was fun. Dolly knew that "little girls should be seen and not heard." When Grandmother and Mother were talking she kept as still as any mouse, but when just she and Grandmother were together she could talk as much as she wanted to. She could ask questions, too. Dolly liked to ask questions.

"Are we really going to make candles tomorrow morning?" she began soon after they started to Grandmother's.

Grandmother nodded.

"How do we make them?"

"You'll see."

"Is it much work?"

Grandmother nodded again.

Dolly jounced up and down on the carriage seat. "I like to work." Then she added truthfully, "Sometimes."

Grandmother laughed. "You are honest about it, anyway."

"Why did you wait until chilly weather to make candles?" Dolly asked next. "Why didn't you make some last summer?"

"We didn't need them then. The sun was up before we were. And after we had worked all day we were ready to go to bed before dark."

"It was that way at our house, too," Dolly remembered.

"Besides," said Grandmother, "you can't make good candles in hot weather. They won't harden. And nobody wants to use a soft candle."

"I know. I tried to make a soft one stand up in my candlestick last week, but it kept bending

60

over. And it dropped burning tallow on my hand. It hurt."

Dolly's eyes almost filled with tears again as she remembered how badly it had hurt her. But just then she saw some butterflies. "Oh, Grandmother, look!"

Then a rabbit ran across the road. A bobwhite called from the bushes, "Bob White! Wheat's most ripe!"

So many things were happening Dolly forgot about her burn. She was sorry when the horse turned at last into the lane leading to Grandmother's house.

"Are we here already?"

"It is time," Grandmother said, laughing. "I expect supper is ready and waiting for us."

It was a good supper. There were hot batter bread covered with melting butter, and ham with fried apples. There was a big mug of creamy milk for Dolly.

Dolly enjoyed every bit of it, but before long her head began to nod.

"Sleepy?" asked Grandmother.

"I reckon I am, a little bit."

"No wonder. You've had a long day. Come along, then. We'll let you sleep in my room to-night. Then you won't get lonesome."

Dolly was too sleepy to be lonesome. She was too sleepy even to look around at the big, tall furniture. Grandmother's bed was so high that she had to use a set of steps to get into it. There was room underneath to store away a smaller bed. The smaller bed was called a trundle bed.

Grandmother's maid had pulled the trundle bed out while Dolly was at supper. She had made it up with linen sheets and a good warm blanket. It was just the right size for Dolly.

"I hope you sleep well, my child," said Grandmother.

Dolly slept well. She slept so well she didn't

even hear Grandmother and Grandfather get up in the early morning. The sun had been shining for over an hour before she even opened her eyes.

The maid poured water into the big bowl for Dolly so that she could wash. She helped her pull her petticoats on over her head. She brushed Dolly's curly hair. Then Dolly hurried on into the dining room.

Grandfather was just finishing his breakfast. Grandmother wasn't there.

"Isn't Grandmother going to have any breakfast?" Dolly asked anxiously.

"She ate breakfast a long time ago, you little sleepyhead."

"Where is she now?"

"It is hard to say. When she is getting ready to make candles she could be almost anywhere. Maybe she is out in the washhouse, making sure that the big kettles are ready. Or maybe she has gone to the spinning room to show the girls how

64

to spin thread for candlewicks. Or maybe she has gone down to the carpenter's shop to get him to send up some boards to put on the floor in the washroom."

"Is that where they are going to make the candles, Grandfather?"

"It is, indeed. But your grandmother said for you to be sure to eat your breakfast before you come out."

Fall was certainly a busy time on the farm. Grandfather hurried away before Dolly had even started on her bacon and eggs. But the nearer she came to the end of her own breakfast, the more slowly Dolly ate.

She had told Grandmother that she liked to work—sometimes. This morning just wasn't one of the times. The sun was shining. The breeze was lively. She didn't want to be shut up in the steamy washhouse. She wanted to play outdoors.

"Grandmother didn't say I *had* to come," she

told herself. "I am company. And Mother always tells me that you must let your company do the things *they* want to do. I want to play."

She looked through the window at the big sweet gum tree in the yard. Its bright red leaves were fluttering down in the breeze. What fun it would be to make twig doll babies and dress them in leaf skirts!

"But if I am company, I suppose I ought to act like company." Dolly frowned. She knew perfectly well what a little girl should do if she were truly company. She ought to sit on a stool by the fireplace and stitch on her sampler like a real little lady.

"Only I'm not that much company," Dolly decided quickly. "I am part home folks. That means that I can do home-folksy things, too, if I want to."

She ran down the hall to the front door and opened it enough to squeeze through. She crossed the wide porch and stood at the top of the broad steps.

"What do I want to do?" She thought for a minute. "I'll gather some acorns and make a tea set for my doll at home."

Back home, last week, it *had* been fun to hunt for acorns. They had just begun to fall, a few at a time. But now the ground under the old oak tree was thick with them. She couldn't even pretend that she had to hunt. She could scoop them up with both hands. Shucks! It wasn't any fun to do that. She would rather play something else.

"I'm too big to swing on the gate. But I can play the fence is my horse and I am a grown lady riding over to my cousin's for a dining day."

She climbed to the top rail of the high fence. She sat sideways, but turned her head toward the gate post.

"That is my horse's head. Now, here we go—buckety, buckety, buckety!"

But it was hard to make believe the fence was really moving.

"I'll go down to the wood lot and make me a tree horse, the way Temple does."

She crawled under the bottom rail of the fence and started across the old field. The field was choked with brambles and briars. They caught at her skirt and tore it.

She looked back at the Big House. She could see all the small buildings behind it. There were the kitchen, the smokehouse and the washhouse. Grandmother came to the washhouse door.

Dolly thought her Grandmother was calling her, but she was too far away to be sure.

She had reached the edge of the woods now. The sudden chill after the warm sunlight in the field made her shiver.

She hurried along, looking for just the right tree. It must be strong enough to hold her without breaking. It must be small enough for her to pull over. At last she found just the right one, but after she pulled it down she couldn't climb on. Temple had always been there to help her before. Now, whenever she tried to climb up on her leafy horse, it would slip out from her hands and swish back up. Once it hit against her face.

"It slapped me," Dolly complained. "It slapped me on purpose.

"Oh, well, who wants to go horseback riding? I'd rather go over to the barn and climb up on the hay. Maybe I can find a hen's nest."

She went past the pigpen without even looking in. The big old hogs with their mean-looking little eyes never interested Dolly. Neither did she stop to watch the chickens in the barnyard.

But two big geese watched Dolly. They quickly decided that no little girl belonged in their barnyard. They flapped their wings. They opened their big hard beaks and hissed.

Dolly ran. She ran until her breath came in

little sobs. Her side hurt. She was too frightened even to scream.

At last the geese stopped. They turned and strutted back to the barnyard. They had shown that girl child a thing or two!

Dolly leaned against the smokehouse wall. She was just beginning to catch her breath when a big bell rang. Why—it was dinnertime!

Dolly went slowly into Grandmother's room to wash her hands and smooth her hair. Grandmother's maid clucked when she saw the muddy streaks on her stockings and the tears in her dress. She helped her into a fresh pinafore, though, that hid most of them.

Then Dolly went into the dining room. Grandmother and Grandfather were already sitting at the table.

"Where have you been?" asked Grandmother. It sounded as if she didn't love her granddaughter. Her voice was cold.

70

"Down in the wood lot," stammered Dolly. "And the geese chased me," she added.

"T'ch, t'ch," said Grandfather. He seemed to blame Dolly instead of the geese.

It was a long dinner. Grandfather and Grandmother talked to each other. Neither of them spoke again to Dolly. Their disapproval hurt Dolly worse than a hard slap would have done. She always wanted people to like her. She couldn't stand it when they didn't.

At last dinner was over. Grandmother said, "I must get back to my candlemaking."

"Please, Grandmother," said Dolly in a small voice, "may I come help? I'm sorry about this morning."

Grandmother looked at her doubtfully.

"Please!"

"Wel . . . l . . ."

Dolly went closer. She slipped her hand into Grandmother's.

"All right, then, child." Grandmother gave her hand a forgiving little squeeze. "Come along."

CANDLEMAKING

"We'll stop in the loom room first," said Grandmother. "We need more thread for candlewicks."

The girls in the loom room had been busy while Grandmother was at dinner. They had been spinning a long, thick coarse string. Grandmother cut it into pieces a little more than twice as long as the candles would be.

"As soon as we get to the washhouse," said Grandmother, "we'll make more wicks."

The washhouse was a little house back of the kitchen. There was a roaring fire in its fireplace. Two heavy kettles hung over the fire. There was water in the bottom of the kettles. Cakes of tallow had been put to melt over the water.

The room was full of steam. The melting tallow was smelly, but Dolly didn't even wrinkle her nose. There were so many things she wanted to ask about.

Long boards had been put down the middle of the room. There was a chair at each end of the boards. Two poles ran from the back of one chair to the back of the other. Small rods or sticks rested across the poles. It looked as if a long ladder rested on the two chairs.

"What are the sticks for?" asked Dolly.

"They are the candle rods."

"Why have you got boards on the floor?"

"To catch the tallow when it drops. It is easier to clean the boards than to scrub the whole floor."

"What is tallow, anyway, Grandmother?"

"Tallow is melted beef or mutton fat. We have been saving every scrap we could for weeks. We cooked the fat over the fire in big pots until every bit of grease was melted out.

"We skimmed the melted grease and put it in

73

large pans to harden. We melted and skimmed it again to be sure it was clear."

Grandmother seated herself on a low stool, with a bunch of candle rods in her lap. She picked up one of the pieces of coarse string. She held one end of it in one hand while she twisted it with the other. Then she doubled it and slipped the loop over a rod. When she let go, the string twisted itself back smoothly in the other direction. The candlewick was ready. She put eight wicks on each rod.

"Now you try it," she told Dolly.

It wasn't so easy as it looked. Dolly's wicks twisted into kinks instead of smooth, even lengths like Grandmother's.

But Grandmother said they weren't at all bad for a beginner. "Just try again, child."

She kept at it until Grandmother finally said that they were fit to use.

By this time, too, Grandmother decided that

one of the kettles of melted tallow was ready.
The two servant girls who were helping her lifted
the huge kettle from the fire. They put it on the
floor by the poles. The hot melted tallow was
deeper than the tallest candle.

Each girl took half of the candle rods. They
sat down close by the kettle. Sukey dipped the
wicks on her first rod into the melted tallow.

Then she lifted the rod. She placed it across the two poles. If the tallow dripped, it would fall on the boards.

While Sukey was placing her rod on the poles, Hattie dipped the wicks on her rod into the tallow. They took turns until all the wicks were dipped. By that time the first ones were hard enough to dip again.

Grandmother watched carefully. "That wick is crooked, Sukey."

Sukey waited until the wick was cool enough to touch. Then she pulled it straight.

"Your tallow is growing cool, girls. You had better use the other kettle."

They carried the first kettle back to the fire. They lifted down the second kettle and went on with their work.

"Each time the candles are dipped," Grandmother explained to Dolly, "they get a little thicker. At last they are big enough to use. We let them hang on the rods until they are cold. Then we slip them off. We trim the bottoms evenly, so that they will fit into a candlestick."

"It looks like fun," said Dolly.

"Try it," said Grandmother. "Sukey, let Miss Dolly have your chair."

Sukey was glad to rest for a while. She went to the door for a breath of fresh air.

"Step outside if you want to," Grandmother called, "but close the door. We want the room to be cool enough for the candles to harden, but if they get too hard too quickly they will crack."

Dolly sat down in Sukey's chair. She picked up a rod.

It wasn't so easy as she had thought it would be. It was *very* easy to burn her hand. She might touch the kettle. She might touch the candles. She might let the tallow drip on her fingers.

It wasn't easy to hold the rod so that all the wicks would go down into the melted tallow at once. The wicks mustn't touch each other or the side of the kettle. They must go all the way down. It was messy work.

"I reckon I have worked long enough now," said Dolly.

Grandmother shook her head. "A lady must learn how to do all the things she expects her servants to do."

So Dolly kept on working. Her fingers were greasy. Her hair came down over her face. When she tried to push it back she got grease on both her hair and face. But she kept on working.

"There ought to be an easier way to make candles," she grumbled.

"There is," said Grandmother. "These are just the everyday candles. We pour the company ones into molds. Do you want to learn that way today, too?"

Dolly certainly didn't want to. One way was enough to learn in one day.

By now she was doing better. She was holding the rod straight, so that its ends rested on the edge of the kettle. She could work almost as fast as Hattie.

And, now that she had learned to do it, she found that something interesting had happened. Today had turned into one of the times when she liked to work.

A Bag and Two Babies

GRANDMOTHER WAS pleased that Dolly had worked so hard over the candles. After supper she called, "Come into my room, child."

There was a big chest in Grandmother's room. It was filled with napkins and tablecloths, but other things were tucked away there, too. When Grandmother opened the big chest there was apt to be a present for a little girl.

Dolly hurried into Grandmother's room now. Sure enough, the chest was open and Grandmother was kneeling in front of it. She stood up when Dolly came in. There was something in her hand. "Come here, Dolly," she said.

She had a little box in her h
open for Dolly to see. There wa
a blue stone, like those in Peg's
mother slipped it on Dolly's fi
pin with a blue stone, too.

"I haven't any patience with your mother's ideas," said Grandmother. "A child ought to have pretty trinkets to wear."

Dolly was delighted with her new treasures. She sat on a footstool in front of the fireplace. She held out her ring finger so that she could see it. She doubled her chin to look down at her pin.

After a while, though, she didn't feel so happy. She began to think about Mother.

Mother was Grandmother's little girl, just as Dolly was Mother's little girl. Also, even though Mother was a grown woman, she would mind what Grandmother said. If Grandmother said Dolly should wear the jewelry, Mother would let her wear it.

81

it would make Mother unhappy. She
ally believed that it was better for little girls
not to have any finery.

Dolly didn't want to hurt Mother, but she
didn't want to give up her pretty things either.
She thought and thought about it. At last she
had an idea.

"May I have a piece of cloth, Grandmother?"

"Certainly, my child. What are you going to
do with it?"

"I'm going to make a bag for my pretties."

"That is a good idea," said Grandmother.

She gave Dolly a piece of linen. Dolly made
a little bag. She ran a cord through the top.

"I shall put my pin and my ring in the bag,"
she told herself. "I can slip the cord around my
neck. The bag will be under my dress. Then
Mother can't see it. She won't even know I have
any jewelry. Then, when I get to school, I can
show it to Peg and Nancy."

She played with her new finery until it was time to go to bed. Then she slipped the pin and the ring into her bag. She put it under the pillow of the trundle bed. She wanted to feel that it was close by her, even while she was asleep.

HOME AGAIN

Grandfather was ready to leave early the next morning. Dolly was ready too. Part of the fun of going visiting was getting home again.

Mother was glad to have her oldest daughter back. "Did thee have a good time, dear?"

"Yes, ma'am."

Mother was glad Dolly had had a good time. She hoped she had forgotten about wanting things that little Quaker girls couldn't have. She didn't even notice the cord around Dolly's neck. She couldn't see the little bag hidden beneath the plain gray dress.

Dolly went back to school the next day.

"We're late," said Walter. "Hurry up, Dolly."

Dolly hurried along over the soft pine tags. When she ran she could feel the bag jogging against her body. It gave her an excited, happy feeling.

She could hardly wait until noon hour. "I've got something to show you," she whispered to Nancy and Peg.

She hurried them around the corner of the schoolhouse, where her brothers wouldn't see. She showed them her ring and her pin.

They weren't nearly so excited as she had expected them to be.

"I have a ring like that," said Nancy, "only the stone is bigger."

"Let's play I Spy," said Peg.

Dolly was disappointed. But she liked to play I Spy. Soon she herself almost forgot about the little bag.

"Let's go by the old creek lot on our way home," said Temple. "There are some hickory-nut trees there. I want to see if we are going to have many nuts this year."

They went through the pine woods. They stopped to watch a squirrel high up in a tree. They found a wild grapevine which made a fine swing. At last they came to the grove of hickory-nut trees.

"Good," said Temple. "They have plenty of nuts. We'll come back after the first frost."

Then they raced home.

"Land o' goodness, honey," said Mammy Amy, "where's your mask?"

Dolly had forgotten it.

"But the sun isn't hot any more, Mammy. I won't get any freckles."

"You can't be too sure," said Mammy. "Girl children must be mighty careful of their looks."

She sat down on the porch steps. Dolly sat down on the step below her. She was tired. She leaned back against Mammy's broad lap. She looked up at the sky.

"It's as blue as my ring," she said.

"What's that? Who's got a ring?"

"I have," said Dolly.

She had meant to tell Mammy all along. Mammy would be like Grandmother. She would be glad Dolly had pretty things.

"Look!" Dolly cried.

She reached for the cord around her neck. She would pull the bag out and show it to Mammy Amy.

There wasn't any cord! She felt down inside her dress. There was no bag there!

The cord must have broken while she was playing in the woods. Her pretty new treasures were gone! Dolly burst into tears.

"There, there!" said Mammy Amy.

Dolly was a big girl now, but Mammy picked her up as if she were Baby Mary. She held her in her lap.

"Tell Mammy what you are crying about, honey chile."

Between sobs Dolly told her all about it.

Mammy Amy shook her head. "You poor little lamb!" she sympathized.

At last they heard Mother. calling. "Mammy! Hasn't Dolly come home from school yet?"

Dolly dried her tears quickly. Mother mustn't see them. Dolly went on into the house.

"Good," said Mother. "I was beginning to be worried about you."

Suddenly Dolly was glad she didn't have the little bag. Last night she had been afraid every time Mother looked at her. She had been afraid Mother would see the cord around her neck. It was good not to be worried any more.

All the same, when she went to bed that

night, she missed her treasures. It was hard to feel under the pillow, and to know that nothing was there.

"And it isn't really wicked to like pretty things," she told herself. "When I grow up, I am going to have heaps and piles of them."

HICKORY-NUT BABIES

Dolly told Temple the next day about losing her bag. He thought girls were silly to want to wear jewelry. But he went to the hickory-nut tree with her. They looked under the grapevine swing. They looked everywhere. It was no use. Dolly never saw her little bag again.

At first she wanted to cry whenever she thought about it. But Dolly could never be unhappy for long. She couldn't always have what she wanted, but she could always enjoy the things she had.

And now she had some girls her own age to play with. Every day at school she and Nancy and Peg could play together.

Sometimes they would go out into the big field at noon. They would pick burs from the burdock plant. They would stick them together to make baskets. Sometimes they would go into the woods. They would get pine needles to make necklaces for themselves. Sometimes, in the winter, the pond near the schoolhouse would freeze. Then they could slide across the ice. In the spring they hunted for violets by the brook.

Even after school closed, there was no time to be lonesome. They couldn't see each other every day, but their mothers could take them visiting. The roads were apt to be either dusty or muddy. It took time to get to a friend's home. When you got there, you stayed long enough to make it worth while.

Father had guests. So did Mother. So did the

boys. And Dolly was growing big enough now
to have guests, too.

Nancy's mother came to spend the day with
Mother. Nancy came along to spend the day
with Dolly.

The women sat in the hall. The breeze blew
through from front to back.

There was a breeze down under the oak tree,
too. Dolly and Nancy decided to go down there.

"What shall we play?" asked Dolly.

Nancy was company. She must choose. "Let's
make ourselves some babies to play with."

"What kind of babies?"

"Hollyhock babies are easy to make."

"But they don't last long."

"That's so. We might make some pretty babies
out of corn shucks."

"They get dry so soon. How about a hickory-
nut baby? They are right hard to make, but they
last for years."

"Where can we find hickory nuts?"

"Temple has some left over from last winter. I'll ask him to let us have two."

"I'll go ask your mammy for some cloth while you get the nuts."

The girls spent most of Nancy's visit working on their two dolls.

First, each one took a piece of heavy cloth, about six inches wide. She rolled it into a tight roll. That made the doll's body.

She balanced a hickory nut on top of the roll. She made a narrow, strong band of cloth, and looped it over the nut. The ends came down on each side of the roll. Then, with another band, she tied the ends to the roll, so that the hickory nut was held firmly in place. The band had to be very tight, or the nut would wiggle.

"What kind of baby is yours going to be?"

"A baby with long dresses. Then I won't have to bother about its feet."

92

"I'll make mine a mammy to tend the baby. Her dress will reach the floor, so I won't have to worry about the feet either."

Dolly got a bit of fuzzy white cotton. She stuck it on the top of the hickory nut with a bit of gum from the pine tree near the gate.

"My baby has white hair," she said.

Nancy used a bit of gray wool for the mammy.

Both dolls had to have caps to hide the band that held their heads on. But babies always wore caps and so did mammies. So that was all right.

"Their arms come next. What shall we do to make arms?"

"We'll make two very small rolls, and sew the end of one to each side of the big roll."

That was hard to do, but at last they were fastened on nicely.

"Shall we fix the faces, or dress them first?"

"Maybe we'd better fix the faces. Then we won't get any stain on the dresses."

"We won't have to make a nose. The pointed end of the hickory nut is a good nose."

"Do you suppose we can find any blackberries left? We can stain the cheeks red with blackberry juice."

The blackberries were about gone, but they found enough to stain the cheeks of the hickory-nut babies. There were enough to get all over their fingers, too.

Then Dolly took the dolls to the house. She borrowed Father's quill pen. Very carefully she drew two eyes and a mouth on each nut.

So far the two dolls were just alike. But now they began to dress them.

Dolly made her baby long petticoats. She sewed a long white dress, with tiny tucks, and made a tiny shawl to wrap the baby in.

Nancy made the mammy some stiff white petticoats. She sewed it a dark homespun dress. She made it a big white apron.

94

"The baby is the same size as the mammy," said Dolly.

"And both their faces really look like kittens."

The girls both laughed. The faces *did* look like kitten faces.

"I don't care. I love my hickory-nut baby."

"So do I."

So did Baby Lucy. She held out her hands for one the minute she saw them.

"No, no," said Mother. "It is Sister's baby. Lucy would hurt it."

But Dolly put it into Lucy's hands. "It is just right for a baby to play with. She can't bite it. She can't break it."

"She can get it all mussed up."

"That's all right," said Dolly. "I can make another. Does thee know, Mother, I believe it's more fun to make things than it is to play with them after they're made!"

War and
Scotchtown

IT WAS good that Dolly did like to make things, because that was the way she had to spend most of her time. She learned to knit, so that she could make fine stockings for Mother and the children. She learned to make the pies and cakes that Father liked. She made dresses for the children and fine shirts for Father. She was so busy she had very little time to think about what was happening in the big world outside Father's plantation.

Exciting things were going on in America, but at first she knew very little about them.

She knew, of course, that the men who came

to see Father were worried. They talked a great deal about things she couldn't understand. "Taxation without representation." She didn't know just what that meant.

Then, when she was six years old, there had been a meeting down in Richmond. Mother's cousin went down from Hanover County. His name was Patrick Henry. He had made a speech. He ended the speech with a ringing sentence that children even younger than Dolly could very well understand—"Give me liberty, or give me death."

After that, ever so many things happened. Men and boys from all over Virginia were going away to war.

It took a long time for news from the army to get back home. Letters were sent by somebody on horseback, or in slow stagecoaches. Sometimes it would be weeks after a battle before the people at home heard about it.

The Payne family waited very anxiously for news. And while they waited, they worked.

SCOTCHTOWN

One day when Dolly was about seven years old, Mother said to her, "Our large family needs a bigger house. Father has bought Scotchtown plantation. It is Patrick Henry's old home. Since he became governor, he does not need it."

Scotchtown! Dolly could hardly believe it was to be her new home. Why, it had nineteen rooms!

Patrick Henry had stopped at Grandmother Coles's one time when Dolly was visiting there. He had told her many interesting tales about his home. And now she would actually *live* there!

Mammy Amy took charge of the moving, but there was plenty of work for all. Finally the packing was done. Furniture and trunks were loaded on wagons. The Payne family rode in their coach. The journey into western Hanover County took one whole day. Finally, at dusk, they spied the old mansion on a hilltop.

The whole family was very weary from the long, jolting ride. However, they were curious about their new home. The children scrambled out of the coach. They ran here and there, exclaiming over all the strange new sights.

The house was over a hundred and fifty years old. The walls were of brick below and clapboard above. It had a peaked roof. Many of the nineteen rooms had fireplaces.

Walter and Temple raced downstairs. They discovered a dungeon below. It was cobwebby, dark, and cold.

They hurried back upstairs and explored outside. "Here are stables for our horses," said Walter, "and cabins for the slaves."

Walter and Dolly walked through the wide hall. It ran from the front to the back of the house. They remembered a tale that Patrick Henry had told them.

When Patrick Henry owned Scotchtown, the British general, Tarleton, and his men had invaded the countryside. At Scotchtown they came on horseback through the front door. They clattered through the hall and out the back door.

Mammy Amy and the husky slaves soon had the furniture in place. Everyone in the family who was old enough stowed away his own belongings. Soon they felt very much at home.

In the evenings they sat around the huge fireplace in the kitchen-house. They studied, munching apples or eating popcorn. Mother sewed or knitted. Father read or kept his books.

One stormy night they were sitting before the blazing fire. All except Father. He had gone to a plantation several miles away on business. He would stay there overnight.

The wind made spooky noises outside. A dog

barked. A loose shutter banged somewhere. Mother said, "I'm glad thee are all inside tonight. I wish Father were here."

Dolly was helping Anna to hem a towel. The boys were reading, stretched out on the floor before the hearth.

Suddenly a Negro boy threw open the door. He was out of breath. He cried out, "The British

soldiers are on the plantation! They'll kill us all! They burned the barns and cabins. They'll come to the house next!"

"We must hide," said Mother, picking up the baby. "But where can we go?"

"Why not the dungeon, Mother?" said Dolly. "We can get there fast."

So Mother headed a small procession from the kitchen-house into the big house. Temple and Dolly led the way through the dark hallway to a secret panel near the door. Temple, with Walter and Dolly, had discovered the spring in the carved woodwork. When it was pressed, the paneling slid back. Even a grownup could squeeze through the hole. Then it was easy to go on into the dungeon.

As Mother and the children groped through the darkness, they heard shots just outside the house. The last person passed through the opening. Walter slid the panel back into place.

It was cold and damp in the dungeon. His teeth chattering, Walter said, "We must stay right here all night. They can't find us, I'm sure."

They tried to make themselves comfortable, but the hours seemed like years. Mammy Amy had snatched up some food before she left the kitchen-house. She fed the youngsters. Then they lay down on blankets which Mother had brought along.

Dolly tried hard to sleep, but she lay wide awake, wondering if the soldiers would burn the house. By daylight she was chilled and stiff.

As soon as light shone through the tiny windows, Mother said, "Let us try the paneling now. We must go and see if the soldiers have left us our house."

Slowly the little procession filed back up the stairs. Temple pressed the spring and the panel slid back. One by one they squeezed through.

They could hardly believe their eyes! The

soldiers had ripped sofas open with their swords. They had turned over tables and chairs. They had slashed pictures and broken dishes. Tarleton and his men had ridden through the wide hall once again!

The enemy had gone on to the kitchen-house. They had taken all the hams hanging there to cure. They had carried away all the flour, rice, and corn meal.

"Our house is almost ruined," said Mother. "However, we should be grateful that it was not burned and we were not harmed. Pray thee that thy father was also spared harm from the wicked soldiers."

Father was safe at the plantation where he had spent the night. It was late the next afternoon when he returned home. He was shocked when he saw the damage to their house.

It took many days to get the house back in order. Everybody worked, even the younger children. Lucy carded wool. Dolly spun it into curtains and tablecloths. Father and the older boys repaired the furniture. Mother seemed to be everywhere at once.

Father and the boys soon finished with the furniture. He then directed the slaves in building new barns and cabins.

The damage to their home was great. The Payne family was thankful, though, that they were all spared and could work to restore it.

FATHER'S PLAN

Little Mary was learning to sew now. Dolly had been teaching her how. Mary had hemmed a handkerchief for Father all by herself. She was very proud of it.

Father said it was a fine handkerchief. "Thee is a very clever child with thy needle."

"I like to sew," said Mary, "but I wish I could

have pretty things to sew on the way other girls do. Dolly wishes she had pretty things to sew on, too. Doesn't thee, Dolly?"

Dolly certainly did, but she knew it would hurt Mother for her to say so. Besides, she didn't need to say it. Mother knew already how she liked pretty things.

"It is only natural," Mother told Father. "The children can't help wanting the same things the other girls have. I wish we lived where there were more Quaker boys and girls. Then Dolly and Mary wouldn't feel they were different from everybody else."

"I would like to live where there were more Quakers, too," said Father. "It is good to be with people who believe the same things we do. Besides, there is another reason why we should leave Virginia when the war is over."

"Leave Virginia!" cried Dolly. "But this is our home."

106

"I know. And it is always hard to leave home. But tonight I'll try to explain it to thee."

That night, after supper, Mammy Amy put the younger children to bed. The others sat by the big fire. Mother and Dolly were knitting, but they could listen to everything Father said.

"It is hard to explain just what I mean," said Father. "Thee knows, of course, why this war is being fought."

"We want to make America free," said Dolly.

"Exactly."

"We're going to win, too," said Temple. "America will be a free country."

Father shook his head. "How can thee call it a free country when it is possible for one man to own another? I can't believe it is right for anybody to own slaves."

Dolly had never thought of it that way before. "But we *have* to have slaves on a big place like this, Father."

"Yes. That is why I want to move. I want to set my slaves free. Then we can move to some place where there are a good many other Quakers like ourselves."

"Where?" asked Temple.

"There are a good many Quakers in Philadelphia. We could all be happy there.

"When spring comes I want Mother and Walter to go up to Philadelphia for a visit. They can look around for a house for all of us. After the war is over I shall set my slaves free. Then we shall all move to Philadelphia."

THE KEY BASKET

Walter was six years older than Dolly. He could take care of Mother very well on the long trip to Philadelphia.

"Who is going to take care of us while you're gone?" asked Lucy.

108

"Mammy Amy, of course."

But the day before Mother left, she called Dolly to her room. "Thee is growing to be a big girl now. I shall leave the key basket with thee while I'm gone."

The keys to the doors in Dolly's home were six or eight inches long. They were so thick and heavy they couldn't possibly be carried on a key ring. They needed a whole basket.

But it wasn't because they were heavy that Dolly felt so important when she took the basket. It was because she knew what Mother meant. Dolly was to carry the keys. That meant Dolly was to keep house while Mother was gone.

The children all stood at the door to wave good-by. They watched Mother's carriage drive down the lane. They watched it turn into the main highway.

Then Mammy took the baby and the little children back into Mother's room.

"Dolly come, too," begged little Anna.

But her big sister shook her head. "Dolly is going to be too busy. She must keep house while Mother is gone."

UNEXPECTED VISITORS

A fat robin outside Dolly's window waked her the next morning. It was a fine morning for sleeping. She cuddled down under her quilt. There was time for a good nap before Mammy called her.

Then she remembered she was keeping house. Housekeepers must get up early. She must unlock the linen closet and give out the clean sheets to the servant who made the beds. She must see what Mandy needed for dinner. She must go out to talk with the gardener about the asparagus bed Mother wanted.

Her mind was full of plans. She hurried

downstairs. "I haven't time to eat breakfast, Mammy. Really, I haven't."

"Now, honey, just take your time. This-here house isn't going to run away while you are eating your breakfast!"

After breakfast the boys went off to school. The little girls played out in the sunshine. Dolly started doing the things that she knew Mother did every day.

By eleven o'clock she was ready to rest.

Just then a little Negro boy came hurrying up the walk.

"Miss Dolly, you're going to have company."

"Goodness!" said Dolly. "Who is it?"

"They're two ladies whose carriage broke down, just outside the gate. I heard 'em say they'd come visit with your ma while the coachman fixed it."

"If their carriage is broken down, they will certainly have to stay to dinner."

Dolly hurried out to the kitchen.

"Don't you fret," said Mandy. "You just open up the storeroom and get me some more ham and fixings. Sam, you go with Miss Dolly to fetch and carry for her. While you're gone, I'll fix this-here chicken we were aiming to eat tomorrow. We can just as well roast it today."

"Will it get done in time?" asked Dolly anxiously.

"Yes'm. If I had to roast it on a spit, like we used to do, 'twould take too long. But this new roasting kitchen your ma bought me will cook it in less than no time."

She brought out a metal box with one side missing. A pointed rod ran through the box.

By the time Sam and Dolly got back to the kitchen, the chicken was ready to roast. Dolly watched while Mandy fastened it on the rod. Then she put the roasting kitchen down on the floor with the open side right in front of the fire.

112

The heat from the blaze would cook the chicken. There was a place in the bottom of the roasting kitchen to catch the drippings. There was a little door in the top. Mandy could open this when she wanted to baste the chicken.

"Now you stay right here and tend it!" Mandy told Sam.

He liked to be near the warm fire. He sat down on the floor by the roasting kitchen. Every little while he would turn the chicken so that it would cook on both sides.

"You run along," Mandy told Dolly. "Go dress up before the company gets here."

Dolly hurried to her room. She wished she had a gay-colored dress to wear. She wished for some pretty lace for her cap. Still, her gray satin dress was pretty. It had elbow sleeves and a square neck. Mammy helped slip it on. There was no time to curl her hair. The ladies had arrived before she could even brush it smooth.

Dolly hurried downstairs into the hall. She curtsied to Mother's friends. She told them she was sorry Mother wasn't home, but she hoped they would stay to dinner just the same.

They sat in the big hall and talked. It was a beautiful spring day.

"Would you like to see Mother's garden?" asked Dolly.

They went to walk in the garden.

"Why, your peas are already up two inches!"

Dolly knew the old gardener would be proud. She herself was proud.

The honeysuckle vines were green. They found several violets. A bluebird perched on a bare branch of the redbud tree. He seemed to be almost as happy as Dolly.

Dinner was ready when they went back to the house. And not long after dinner the coachman came to say that the carriage was fixed.

"I am sorry to have you go," said Dolly.

114

"We hate to go, too. I shall write your mother that her daughter is a charming hostess."

After the ladies were gone, Mammy called Dolly back into Mother's room. "You better come rest yourself, child. You must be plumb tuckered out."

"Having company *does* make me tired," Dolly agreed, "but it is lots of fun. I like it."

Jack Jouett's Ride

MOTHER CAME back from Philadelphia with all sorts of stories about what she had seen there. "I know thee will like it," she told Dolly. "And Father will like it, too. If only this terrible war were over!"

The war wasn't over, though. Instead, it came nearer to Dolly than ever before. The enemy had reached Richmond, which was only twenty miles away.

The Payne family waited anxiously each day for news.

"We haven't heard a word for nearly a week," Dolly told Temple one day in June.

116

There had been a heavy shower that morning and the road was muddy. Dolly never expected to leave the house after a bad shower. She didn't expect visitors, either. She took it for granted that the road would be so bad a carriage couldn't get through.

But it was different with men on horseback. Temple was anxious for news, too. "I am going to ride down to the courthouse," he said. "Maybe there will be some mail."

"I'd like so much to hear from Aunt Dorothea," said Dolly.

Aunt Dorothea had married Patrick Henry. He was a member of the Virginia General Assembly now. Since the enemy had taken Richmond, the Assembly was having its meetings at Charlottesville.

"Be careful, son," said Mother. "It is very easy for a horse to stumble on these muddy roads."

"Yes'm. I'll be careful."

117

When Temple came back he was splashed and muddy, but he was too excited to notice the condition of his clothes.

"What do you think? Colonel Tarleton has tried to capture Thomas Jefferson!"

Dolly was playing with the baby. She was so startled she almost let the child drop. "Oh, Temple! He didn't do it, did he?"

"Indeed, he didn't."

"Goodness, but thee frightened me! What happened?"

"Well, he started out with about two hundred and fifty men. They were going to ride as fast as they could to Charlottesville. Colonel Tarleton thought he could get there before anybody knew he was coming. Then he could take Governor Jefferson and Patrick Henry and all the men in the Assembly prisoners. Virginia would be left without any leaders at all.

"And he would have done it, too, if it hadn't been for Captain Jack Jouett."

"I know him," said Dolly. "He came to see Father not long ago. He has the most beautiful horse I've ever seen!"

"He certainly has. It is the finest nag in seven counties. Well, Captain Jack was at Cuckoo Tavern. He saw Colonel Tarleton when he went by. He suspected what the colonel was trying to do. So he jumped on his horse and took a short cut through the woods. He rode all night."

"That short cut is a terrible road. It is all rocks and stones."

"That's right. Captain Jack's face is all cut and scratched, too, where the branches of the trees slashed in his face in the dark as he rode under the trees. It must have been pitch-black dark in the forest, but, between nine o'clock and sunrise, he rode forty miles! He reached Governor Jefferson's home, and told him the soldiers

119

were coming. Mr. Jefferson had time to get away. Then Captain Jack rode on to Charlottesville. Most of the men there got away, too."

"Did Cousin Patrick Henry get away?"

Temple nodded.

"Oh, I'm glad," said Dolly. "But what is thee laughing at?"

"Do you remember General Stevens?"

"Is he the one who looks like an old countryman?"

"That's the one. Well, after Captain Jack had warned the legislature, he and General Stevens were riding along the road together when here came some of Tarleton's men. General Stevens is an important man. Tarleton would have liked to take him prisoner. But Captain Jouett had on a fine red coat and a hat with a plume, and the soldiers thought he was the important one. They thought General Stevens was just an old farmer. So they dashed after Captain Jouett.

120

He just led them on until he'd made sure that General Stevens had turned up a side road and escaped. Then he just started that horse of his really to galloping. He left the soldiers behind in no time."

"Oh!" exclaimed Dolly.

The baby had been listening to the story, too. She was too little to understand what it was about, but she knew some of the words. And they gave her an idea.

"Baby wants to play horse," she told Dolly.

Dolly laughed. "All right. Thee is Captain Jack Jouett."

She balanced the child on her knee.

"Here we go to Charlottesville. Watch out for the rocks and stones."

She bounced the baby up and down. The child squealed with delight. It was a fine game.

122

Freeing the Slaves

AT LAST the war was over. "Now," thought Dolly, "everything will be just like it used to be. Maybe Father will forget about moving."

But he didn't. Night after night, Dolly could hear him talking to Mother after the children had gone to bed. Nearly every day there would be visitors who came to see him about his plans.

Dolly liked visitors. She was old enough now to eat dinner with the grownups. Of course, she must be very quiet. She could listen, though.

Some of the guests were Quakers like Father. They would talk seriously. "It is a good thing that thee plans to do, Friend Payne."

Some of the other men got very angry. "You're crazy, I tell you!" they shouted.

Dolly never liked it when people quarreled. It made her feel uncomfortable. She was glad when it was time for Mother and her to leave the table. The men sat on and on, talking and arguing. From the next room she sometimes heard them shouting.

They couldn't change Father's mind.

"When thy father thinks a thing is right, he is going to do it," said Mother.

Of course Dolly knew she ought to be glad she had a father like that. She couldn't help wishing, though, that the things he thought were right wouldn't make other people so angry.

CHEERS AND TEARS

At last Father finished his plans. Then he called his slaves together. They stood down in

124

the yard, close by the porch. Father stood on the steps. He spoke so they could all hear him.

"You have been good servants to me. You have done your work well. But I do not believe it is right for a man to own slaves. I am going to give you your freedom. That means you may go where you want to. I shall give each of you a piece of paper that will show you are freedmen. And I will help you to buy little farms, where you can live and work for yourselves."

One of the Negroes cheered. Another was so happy she cried. The little children didn't know what it was all about, but they cheered, too.

Mammy Amy, though, didn't think it was a good idea at all. "I don't care if he is your pa," she told Dolly. "He's crazy. And he needn't think he can set *me* free! I won't stand for it!"

"Why, Mammy, doesn't thee want to be free?"

"Huh! You know as well as I do that your ma can't get along without me! If you move from this-here place, who's going to take care of the children along the way? Who's going to help her get the new house straight? She can't get along without me, and you know it! Set old Mammy Amy free? I'd just like to see anybody try doing it!"

She looked so fierce that Dolly could hardly help laughing.

Father didn't laugh, though. He talked with Mammy for a long time. He tried to explain things to her. Mother tried to explain things, too. It didn't do a bit of good.

Mammy shook her head so hard her kerchief almost fell off.

All the next day, she went around muttering to herself. "Huh! Set *me* free! Let's see 'em try to do it!"

"I don't know what to do," said Father. "I can't set her free if she won't let me."

"She's right about one thing," Dolly told him.

"Mother will certainly need her to help in our new home."

"Suppose we pay Mammy regular wages just as we would if we hired somebody who was free," suggested Mother.

"We could do that," Father agreed. "I would feel much better if I didn't own any slaves. If she insists, that will be the next best thing. Tell her she can stay with us, Dolly, but that we shall pay her wages every week."

Mammy didn't think much of that idea, either, but she gave in. "All right. He can pay me wages if he wants to, but he can't make me spend one cent of 'em."

MAMMY AMY'S WILL

Walter was laughing when Dolly met him in the hall the next day. "What do you think Mammy is up to now?"

"Goodness knows. What?"

"She wants me to write her will for her."

"Is thee going to?"

"Uh-huh. Why not?"

"She can't even sign it. She doesn't know how to write her name."

"She can make a cross mark. And we'll write by it, 'Amy—her mark.'"

So Mammy Amy made her will. She asked that every cent she left at her death would be given to Mother.

Every week Father paid her her wages.

Off to Philadelphia

"Look, Dolly, I'll need my gun."

"Why can't I take my chickens, sister?"

"Thee'll *have* to make room for my footstool."

The Payne family was moving to Philadelphia. The hall was filled with big boxes. Mammy was busy packing. Mother had asked Dolly to tell Mammy which of the children's things should go into the boxes and which should be left behind. The children wanted to take everything.

"If you don't run along and leave me alone," said Dolly, "you'll drive me wild."

"You run along yourself," said Mammy. "I can finish up now without you."

So Dolly ran along. Little Anna caught hold of her hand. Wherever Big Sister Dolly went, Little Sister Anna was going, too.

The big rooms were half-empty. They no longer looked like home.

Dolly and Anna went down to the springhouse for a last drink of the cool, fresh water.

"After we're gone," Dolly said, "this spring will keep on bubbling away, just as if nothing had changed. It won't miss us a bit." Her voice sounded sad.

Anna began to feel mournful too. "It is a naughty old spring," she said.

Dolly laughed. "I was silly to talk like that, because we won't miss the spring any more than it misses us. There are plenty of good wells in Philadelphia."

There was a big dipper on the wall of the springhouse. It was made from a gourd. Dolly dipped up a cool drink for Anna.

130

"I don't want to go away," said Anna. "I want to live here at Scotchtown forever and ever. Doesn't thee, Dolly?"

Dolly shook her head. "Maybe we'll be homesick just at first, but it is foolish to think there is only one place in the world where thee can be happy, Anna. I believe I could be happy almost anywhere."

They started very early the next morning. Mother, Mammy Amy, and the girls rode in the coach. The youngest children didn't take up much room. Even then there was little space left for the boxes and bags they had to carry.

Father and the boys rode horseback. Then there were the wagons to carry their furniture and their trunks.

"We look like a parade," said Walter.

Anna and Lucy were so excited they could hardly sit still. They wanted to look out of both windows at once.

131

"There is the road that goes to Grandmother Coles's house!"

"There's the old persimmon tree!"

"Look, there's Zeke! Good-by, Zeke!"

After a very few miles, Lucy leaned back. "I've never been any farther than this before."

Dolly hadn't been much farther herself. She had never seen a really big city. She was almost as excited as the little girls.

Soon they came to a rocky place in the road. How they rattled and bounced! At first the children thought it was fun. Then one of the carriage wheels struck a big stone. The carriage swayed so far the children slid into a heap by the downside window.

"We're turning over!" cried Anna.

"Quick!" said Dolly. "Move as far as you can over to the other side of the carriage. Lean out the window over on that side."

Slowly the carriage righted itself.

132

"Did we really help?" asked Anna.

"I don't know," Dolly answered honestly. "Maybe we don't weigh enough to make much difference, but certainly we didn't do any harm. And it helped *us,* anyway. Weren't you frightened when the carriage started to turn over?"

"I was, indeed," said Anna.

"But what happened when you tried to help?"

"I was so busy I forgot about being afraid."

Dolly laughed. "So was I. And I reckon that is what happens to most people."

"Well, maybe it is a good idea, but I'd just as soon not have to try it out any more. Let's hope we don't hit any more big rocks like that one."

For a while they didn't. Instead, the roadbed was filled with small, rounded rocks. They made the wheels rattle. They made the children jounce around.

"We're bouncing around like black-eyed peas in a kettle of boiling water," Lucy decided.

"Look!" said Anna. "If you hold your mouth a little open, you can make your teeth rattle."

This was fun for a while, but all of them were glad when at last they came to a smooth stretch of road. Mother leaned back and closed her eyes.

Soon the carriage came to a steep hill.

"Let's get out and climb the hill," Dolly said. "It will save the horses and give us a chance to stretch ourselves, too."

It was good to walk a bit and limber up.

"Let's run down the hill on the other side," suggested Anna.

That was fun, too, but at the foot of the hill they had to climb back into the carriage. A brook ran across the road. It was wide, but it wasn't very deep. There was a splash and a spatter. Then the horses had pulled them out on dry land.

The next stream they came to was deeper. The carriage wheels went down, down, until the water came up to the floor of the carriage.

"Look!" cried Lucy. "It is coming in through the cracks!"

"Quick!" said their mother. "Put your feet up on the cushions!"

It was hard to keep their balance with their feet stretched out like that. They bumped against each other. They giggled and laughed.

Soon, though, they were on dry land once more. The water leaked out of the carriage. They could put their feet down again.

"Goodness!" said Anna. "I hope we won't come to any streams that are deeper than that."

"We shall, though," said Mother. "That was just a creek. We have several rivers, too, that we must cross."

"However are we going to do it?"

"Thee will see."

At last they did come to a big river. There was no bridge across it. It was too deep for the horses to get to the other side.

"We'll just have to stop," said Anna.

There was a big tree by the side of the road. A horn was hanging in the tree. Father blew the horn hard.

There was a house on the other side of the river. A man came out to the riverbank when he heard the horn.

The children could see a big flatboat on his side of the river.

"Only it is really more like a raft than a boat," said Mary.

The man got on the boat. He had a long pole. He shoved the pole down onto the bottom of the river and pushed the boat along. At last he reached their side.

Then the Payne coach was driven onto the boat. The man poled them back across the river. It took several trips across to carry horses, riders, and wagons.

Father had decided to make the trip in June.

The long wet spell in May was over then. The roads weren't muddy. But they were dusty! Sometimes Dolly wondered if she would ever be able to wash her face and hands clean again.

Not all of the trip was unpleasant. It was fun to ride in the early morning. The birds were singing. The breeze blew through the windows of the coach. It was pleasant to go through the green pine woods.

One day they came to a bigger river than they had ever seen before.

"It is the Potomac River," said Mother.

"It is beautiful," said Dolly. "Wouldn't that be a lovely place for a home, up on that hill!"

Temple was riding by the side of the coach. "You never like a place until you have some people in it," he teased. "I suppose on the other side of the river you'd put a whole city."

"It would be a good place for one," said Dolly, seriously.

138

They all laughed. The idea of a city on those green fields and rolling hills was funny.

It seemed to Dolly as if the trip would never end. The children were growing cross and fretful. But at last, one morning, Father said: "If we don't break down, we'll be in Philadelphia by nightfall."

How excited the children were! They could talk of nothing else all day. They began to play a game. "What will you like best about Philadelphia?"

"I shall like it because I can go to school again," said Temple. "It is so big there will be schools to teach anything I want to know."

"I shall like it," said Mother, "because there will be Quakers there. It will be good to be with other Friends."

"I shall like it," said Dolly, "because there will be plenty of people there. I have always liked people."

The road turned a curve. They could look down on the valley of the river. And on the other side, they could see the roofs and steeples of Philadelphia.

Their journey was over.

New Home–New Friends

THE PAYNE family's new home was quite different from the Scotchtown mansion. The brick house was tall and narrow. It was exactly like the whole row of Quaker homes. Dolly cried, "They all look alike!"

The children stood drooping while their father walked up the white steps to the tiny porch. He opened the door into the narrow hall. They trooped in and started to explore this strange house. There was an iron Franklin stove in the living room. Mother explained, "It is called a Franklin stove because Benjamin Franklin invented it."

141

There was a huge fireplace in the back room. This room would be their kitchen and family room. Father made a fire in the fireplace to take the chill from the room. They were almost too tired to enjoy it. Usually they made up stories about the strange pictures they imagined they saw in the flames.

Suddenly there was a knock at the door. Mr. Payne opened it. A pleasant-looking woman and two young girls were standing there. The woman was carrying a large basket. She smiled and said, "We bid thee welcome to thy new home. These are my daughters, Sally and Nancy. We thought thee would be tired and hungry. We've brought thee a hot meal."

Mother had met Mrs. Elizabeth Drinker when she visited Philadelphia before they moved. Now she presented her family. Soon they were all chattering like old friends.

Mother helped Mrs. Drinker to unpack the

basket. Mammy Amy made hot tea. The hungry family enjoyed rye bread, cheese, and sausage. Still hot in an earthen pot was Philadelphia pepper pot, a sort of stew made of beef tripe, tomatoes, peppers, spices, and tiny dumplings. The Paynes had never tasted it before. They thought it was delicious. They all felt much better after the warm food and tea. They were happy to have new friends already in this strange town.

Sally and Nancy were near Dolly's age. Sally was the older. She had blonde hair and blue eyes. Nancy was not quite so pretty, but she was jolly and clever.

Sally smiled at Dolly and her brothers and sisters. "It will be fun having all thee Paynes in our school. We like meeting new boys and girls," she said.

Mrs. Drinker picked up the nearly empty basket. "It is time that we leave thee to get some rest," she said. "Come on, girls."

"Good night, all," cried Sally. "We will see thee tomorrow, Dolly."

"Scrubbing steps," Nancy said slyly.

Then they explained that scrubbing the white marble steps was an old custom. The Quakers kept them spotless. No matter what the weather was, twice a week the steps were scrubbed and scoured. Usually the girls of the family took turns at the task.

Next morning Dolly took a mop and a bucket of steaming soapy water and scrubbed the steps. Two doors away, Nancy was already busy on her hands and knees. She hummed a gay tune as she worked. When she saw Dolly, she cried, "Good morning, Dolly! I hope thee slept well."

Dolly looked up and down the street. On every porch, a girl was busily scrubbing and scouring white steps. As they toiled, they chattered back and forth.

Living in the city was certainly different from

144

living in the country. Sometimes Dolly felt almost as if she must be another person.

She had always been used to plenty of space. The city house seemed little and crowded.

And the noises! There had been plenty of noise in the country. In the morning the roosters would wake her before the sun was up. She would hear the cows being driven to pasture. There were the ducks and the geese and the birds and the dogs. She had been so used to them all, she hardly knew they were there.

But the city noises nearly drove her wild. Carriages and carts rattled up and down the streets. There were bells of every kind—fire bells, church bells, the market-house bell.

There was another bell, too. The crier of news went through the streets ringing his bell. Men and boys would run to the street corners to hear him tell what had happened. It vexed Dolly.

"Whenever I want one of the boys to do

something, he is nowhere around. He is off to hear the news."

But Mother just laughed. "Back in Virginia, they had to ride all the way to the courthouse to find out what had happened. It saves us a lot of time when they just have to run down to the corner to hear it."

The truth was, Dolly was cross because she was lonesome. Back in Virginia she didn't see many people, but she knew everybody she saw. In Philadelphia there were over four thousand homes. She couldn't expect ever to know the people who lived in all of them. Right now she didn't know anybody. The sight of so many strange faces frightened her.

Then, too, it had turned very cold a few days after they reached their new home. It was so cold Mother had to build a fire in the parlor! A fire in July! This must be a strange town!

Then, before they had grown used to the cold,

146

it was hot again. City heat was different from country heat. The houses were too close together for the breeze to get around them. The pavements soaked in the sunlight. They stayed hot after the day was over.

City folk had no cool springhouse where they could keep their milk when it was hot. It would sour in spite of everything Dolly could do.

"I don't like this place. That is all there is to it," she decided to herself.

FIRST DAY MEETING

When First Day came, Dolly went with Father to meeting. The Free Quaker Meeting House was a very plain little building. There was no pulpit. There was no choir. There was no preacher.

The women all sat on one side of the church. Their dresses were mostly of soft gray. Many

147

of them had white kerchiefs. All of them wore hoods or bonnets.

The men sat on the other side of the church. They, too, were very plainly dressed. They wore high hats with broad brims.

There were no hymns. There was no preaching. Everyone sat, waiting. If the Spirit moved someone to speak, that person would speak. Sometimes it would be a man. Sometimes it would be a woman. Sometimes nobody would speak. Then each person would worship God quietly, by himself.

One couldn't stay cross in the peace and quiet of the Meeting House. Dolly forgot she was lonesome and homesick.

Over on the men's side of the church, Father stood up. He took off his hat with the broad brim. He began to talk.

He told how he felt about slavery. He told why he had come to Philadelphia.

Dolly had heard it all before. But the others hadn't. They listened seriously. More than one nodded his head as if to say, "Thee has done the right thing, Friend Payne."

"Why," thought Dolly, "it is silly of me to fret. Of course he's right."

She had a funny grown-up feeling, as if Father were her little boy. She wanted to take care of him.

"What difference does it make whether I'm lonesome or not? It won't be long before I know people. Father is happy here. And he has done what he thinks is right. Why, I am *glad* we have moved to Philadelphia!"

AT THE SHOPS

The next day the sun was shining. There was a good breeze. It was neither too hot nor too cold.

"Come along," said Dolly to little Anna. "It

is a fine day for a walk. I don't care if we don't know anybody. We can have a good time just by ourselves."

Anna was quite ready to go for a walk. They started off together.

"Where are we going?" asked Anna.

"Let's go to the shops first."

Anna knew very little about shops. Dolly herself knew very little about them. Back home, in Virginia, they had grown their own food. They had made their own clothes. They had made their own soap and brooms and other things to use around the house. When they wanted very special things, Father ordered them all the way from England. Dolly had never been inside a really big store.

Things were different when you lived in the city. Already Mother was beginning to need things from the shops. She had asked Dolly to get her some white muslin for a kerchief.

There were so many shops it was hard to decide which one to try first. It was still harder to choose the muslin Mother would like best.

While they were waiting for their package, they had a chance to look around. Dolly had never seen such beautiful things in all her life. There were bolts of rich red satin. There were bolts of purple velvet. There were brocades stiff with embroidered flowers.

"Look in the next room, Dolly," whispered little Anna. "There are some grown ladies playing with a doll baby."

"Oh, no, darling."

"They are so, too. Look."

There was a little parlor in the back of the store. The door was open, so anyone could see inside. Three young ladies were seated on a sofa. They certainly had a doll baby. They were passing it around to one another, and they were all talking at once.

152

"The sleeves are tight."

"See how the hair is worn in curls at each side of the neck."

"I like the way the gown is looped up over the petticoat."

The storekeeper saw the girls watching. "That is our newest fashion baby," he said. "She has just been sent over from London. She is dressed in the very latest style. The ladies pay to look at her. Then they know how to have their own dresses made."

"Oh," said Dolly.

"Don't children ever have a chance to play with her?" asked Anna.

"Not now. But I shouldn't be surprised if my own little girl finally gets her after her clothes go out of style."

Anna felt happier. It didn't seem right for the baby to belong just to grown people.

"Now where shall we go?" asked Anna.

"Let's walk on Chestnut Street."

"It would be prettier down by the river."

Dolly shook her head. She knew that the fashionable young ladies always took their afternoon walks on Chestnut Street. She wanted to see them and their finery.

They were certainly worth watching. They wore full skirts of bright-colored silk. Their hair was piled high on their heads. Their bonnets were sights to behold.

The young men's waistcoats were as bright as the women's dresses. They wore buckles at their knees. They wore buckles on their shoes. They bowed low to the young ladies.

"There are the ladies who were looking at the fashion baby," said Anna.

Sure enough—there they were. There were some young men with them. They were laughing and talking as they passed Dolly and Anna.

"One of those girls didn't look a bit older than

154

thee is," said Anna. "And she is going to the Assembly Ball tomorrow night. I heard what they were saying. Would thee like to go to a ball, Dolly?"

"I certainly would," said Dolly.

She couldn't help but feel a little sorry for herself again as they walked on. Then she remembered that yesterday she had made up her mind not to fret.

"But there are plenty of other ways to have a good time," she added very quickly.

NEW FRIENDS AND FUN

Mammy Amy was waiting for them when they reached home.

"I'm glad you've come," she told Dolly. "You've got company."

"Company? Me?"

"Uh-huh. It's Mrs. Drinker's daughter that's

just come home from a long visit down in the country."

Dolly hurried into the front room. Mrs. Drinker and her daughter Sally were there. They were talking to Mother.

Sally had been away in the country ever since soon after the Paynes had moved to the city. "She just got back yesterday," said Mrs. Drinker. "She wanted to come to see thee right away."

"I knew thee hadn't had a chance to meet any girls yet. I was afraid thee might be getting lonesome," Sally told Dolly.

"I was," said Dolly.

"Well, we shan't let thee stay that way long. Would thee like to go for a drive tomorrow? Brother will come by for thee. And I'll ask Polly Wells and Josey Sansom and some of the others to go along, too. We'll go down to our place in the country. We'll have tea and play games there. Would thee like to go?"

156

"Oh, yes," said Dolly, "that will be fun."

It was fun. They drove down in the early afternoon. The big lawn of the Drinkers' home in the country was a fine place for games. Button, Button, Who's Got the Button, Grind the Bottle, Forfeits—they played them all. Then they sat on the porch steps and sang.

Dolly felt as if she had known these boys and girls all her life.

It was nearly dark when they reached home. Anna was already in bed. She was wide-awake, though. She wanted Dolly to tell her everything that had happened.

Dolly began to get ready for bed, too. She brushed her long, black hair while she talked.

She told Anna everything they had done. "We certainly did have a lot of fun."

A carriage went by under their window. They could hear the wheels rattling over the stones in the street.

"Maybe that is the same girl we saw yester-day," said Anna. "Maybe she is on her way to the Assembly Ball."

"Maybe so," said Dolly.

"Does thee wish thee was going, too?"

"Not tonight. I'm too tired. What I told thee yesterday was right. There is more than one way to have a good time."

Dolly Grows Up

It was hard to tell when she changed from a girl into a young lady. Sometimes Dolly wasn't sure, herself, just which she was. She still liked to romp with the children, but she liked to do grown-up things, too. She liked to feel that the young men were looking at her when she came from the Meeting House on First Day. And she liked *very* much to feel that they thought she was attractive.

There was one young man especially. His name was John Todd. "I *know* he looks at me more than he does at the other girls," thought Dolly. "I'm not conceited. But he really does."

It was hard, now, to remember that she had ever been lonesome in Philadelphia. She had many friends. And there was always something exciting to do.

Peace had been declared between America and England. There was going to be a big celebration. Workmen were busy on Market Street. They built a great wooden arch over the street. On the sides of the arch were big paintings of Washington and other heroes.

The arch would be lighted with many lamps. On top there were fireworks, ready to be set off as soon as it was dark.

Dolly had been to a party that afternoon. The girls had been very busy sewing and talking. Of course, they stayed much later than they had meant to stay.

It was nearly dark when Dolly started home. Already people were hurrying toward Market Street to see the celebration.

160

"I must hurry, too," thought Dolly to herself. "Maybe I can get home in time to get the children to the window. We can see the fireworks over the housetops."

Market Street was so crowded it was hard to get across. Then something happened.

They were lighting the lamps under the big arch. Somebody dropped a lamp. The flames ran up the side of the arch. The pictures caught fire. Then the flames reached the top. They set off the fireworks all at once.

The rockets fired down into the middle of the big crowd. Women screamed. Many people had come with horses and carriages to see the fireworks. The horses were frightened by the noise and the rockets. They tried to plunge through the crowd.

People and animals began to rush past Dolly. They almost knocked her down. She shrank back against a wall.

Then she heard someone say, "Don't be afraid,
Dolly Payne. I will get thee safely out of the
crowd."

There was young Friend John Todd. Dolly
was certainly glad to see him.

He put her hand under his arm. He pushed

their way through the crowd. Soon they were safe at home.

"Will thee come in, John Todd?" asked Dolly at the door.

He seemed glad to come in. And Father was glad to see him.

"Father likes John Todd," she thought.

Then she began to tell the children about the excitement at the fire.

"I DON'T WANT TO MARRY ANYBODY"

Things didn't go well with Father in Philadelphia. It had cost a lot to set his slaves free. Moving had cost a great deal, too. And everything was so expensive in the city!

He had to pay house rent. He had to pay wages to the servants. He had to buy all the things they used to grow on the plantation. Why, even chickens were fifty cents apiece!

163

He tried to start out in business. Father knew very little about business and he failed. That took nearly all of the money that the family had left.

Dolly tried to help him every way she could. She was glad when his friends came to see him. That always seemed to cheer him up.

Friend John Todd came often now. Sometimes he would take Dolly for a drive. Other times he would stay and talk with Father.

"Thee must take good care of Father while I am gone," Dolly told him one day.

"Gone where?"

"I am going to visit Aunt Creighton over in Haddonfield for a while."

"I hope thee will have a very good time."

When she went with him to the door that afternoon, he said, "Don't stay away very long, little Dolly Payne."

"John Todd is Dolly's beau," Anna said teas-

164

ingly after he had gone. "He wants to marry our Dolly."

"Nonsense!" said Dolly. "I don't intend to marry anybody."

Mother smiled.

JOHN TODD CALLS ON FATHER

John Todd came to see Father again the next day. He stayed a long time. After he had gone, Father called Dolly to his room. "I have something very serious to tell thee."

"Yes, Father."

"Thee is a young woman, now, Dolly."

Dolly nodded. "I am twenty years old."

"John Todd has asked me for thy hand. He wants thee to become his wife."

"Oh," said Dolly.

"He is a good man. He will make thee a good and kind husband."

"But I am not sure I want to marry."

Father shook his head. "I am not strong," he said. "I should like to feel that there would be someone to take care of thee after I am gone. John Todd will wait for his answer. I hope very much that it will be 'yes.'"

A VISIT TO AUNT CREIGHTON

Aunt Creighton lived across the river. Her husband kept an inn. They enjoyed having young people visit them. They planned parties and thought up new things to do. Dolly knew she would have a fine visit. She was sure it would be easy not to think about John Todd.

The very first day, Aunt Creighton said, "The berries are ripe. It is time to go a-berrying."

There were several young girls who lived near Aunt Creighton. There were several young men, too. They started off, each carrying a pail.

166

Deep back in the woods, the berries grew thick. What a good time they all had!

Dolly found it took a long time, though, to fill her pail, no matter how hard she tried.

"If John Todd were here, he'd help me," she found herself thinking.

Trenton wasn't far away from Aunt Creighton's place.

"Let's drive over there," she said to Dolly. "I want to shop."

Aunt Creighton was a Quakeress, too, but she liked pretty things almost as much as Dolly did.

Dolly had a fine time going through the shops with her. Aunt Creighton didn't mind stopping to look at the beautiful ribbons and laces. She liked them too.

"Look, Dolly, a cap of this lace would be pretty on thy hair."

"John Todd doesn't like lace caps." Dolly spoke before she thought.

"Oh!" said Aunt Creighton.

The mail coach stopped twice a day at the inn. It changed horses there.

There was another cousin visiting at Aunt Creighton's now. "It is fun to ride in the mail coach," she told Dolly. "Thee bounces and jounces so."

"Let's try it," said Dolly.

"Where would we go?"

"We'll ride out in the country a mile or so and walk back to Aunt Creighton's."

"Silly!"

"It's fun to be silly."

They both giggled.

"All right. Let's."

They asked the driver to let them ride with him. He grinned. "Sure."

They rode a mile or two out into the country. They bounced and jounced. And they had a fine time laughing and joking.

"We're acting like two little children."

"Good. Let's forget we're young ladies."

At last the driver stopped the coach and let them out. They had to walk back home.

The sun was setting. The air was cool. It was a pleasant walk. For a while they kept on laughing and talking. Then they grew quiet. They walked for quite a distance without talking.

"A penny for thy thoughts," the cousin said suddenly. Dolly was surprised.

"Why—I was just thinking about Father," said Dolly, slowly.

She was wondering whether John would call on Father that afternoon.

THE ANSWER

The Payne children were glad to have Dolly back home again. They crowded around her, all talking at once.

"Look, Dolly! I finished my sampler while thee was gone."

"Dolly, John cut his finger."

"Dolly, Temple made me a whistle!"

But Father and Mother were very quiet. After dinner Father called Dolly to his room again.

"Well, daughter, does thee have thy answer ready for John Todd?"

"Tell him," said Dolly, "that I shall be glad to do whatever thee thinks is best."

The Story of Dolly Todd

AND SO Dolly Payne and John Todd were married. It was a simple, quiet wedding. There were no flowers or music. Dolly would have liked to wear a beautiful white gown, with a long train and veil. Instead, she wore her regular plain gray dress, with a thin, white kerchief. Her scoop bonnet covered her black curls.

John and Dolly lived in a comfortable, brick, Quaker house. It was exactly like Dolly's first home in Philadelphia, tall and narrow. It, too, had white marble steps.

Inside, the little house was spick and span. Dolly was a good housekeeper and cook.

After their baby boy was born, the young Todds were happier than ever.

One day Anna and Mary came to see Dolly, both quite excited. They first went upstairs to the nursery to admire and pet the baby.

Soon Anna burst out, "I have wonderful news! Thee and I are invited to tea at Mrs. George Washington's tomorrow at four o'clock!"

Dolly tried to act calm and grown-up, but she was very excited at being a guest of Mrs. Washington. She knew they had been invited only because their sister Lucy had married George Washington's nephew, George Steptoe Washington. That made them a sort of "kin folk."

Anna put on her bonnet, saying, "I wish I could wear a pretty hat and gown."

Dolly kissed her sister and said, "Thee looks very pretty, even in thy plain dress and bonnet."

Next day Dolly put on her best dress. It was a trim, gray Quaker costume, with a sheer white kerchief. She wore her big scoop bonnet. Anna looked pretty and sweet in her neat gray dress.

The attractive sisters walked to the home of the President and Mrs. Washington.

Dolly was a bit nervous as they climbed the narrow stairs to an upper hall. At the left was a drawing room filled with guests. Several gentlemen in a group were talking. Many well-dressed ladies chatted as they drank tea and ate cake.

Under a candle-lighted chandelier Martha Washington was seated at the tea table. She was pouring tea from a gleaming silver teapot into delicate china cups.

A lady dressed in black satin came to Dolly and Anna. "I'm Mrs. Knox," she said, smiling. "May I present you to Mrs. Washington?"

Martha Washington greeted the two sisters with a warm smile. She introduced them to young Mrs. Alexander Hamilton. Mrs. Hamilton invited both girls to sit on the sofa beside her.

173

Nellie Custis, Mrs. Washington's granddaughter, brought them cups of fragrant tea. Another young girl served them plum cake.

Dolly was surprised and pleased to know that the President's wife served plain plum cake. It was the same kind that Dolly herself made.

Mrs. Washington left the tea table and came to sit beside Dolly. "How does your sister like her new home in Virginia?" she asked.

Dolly was shy at first, but when Mrs. Washington asked her about her baby and her home, she was no longer timid. She was telling her hostess about little Payne's cute baby tricks when she happened to look toward the doorway.

Just then a tall, white-haired man passed by the door. Dolly knew right away that he was President Washington. She was so thrilled that she jumped up from the sofa. She had forgotten the cup of tea she was holding. Over it went! The tea splashed on her own dress. But worse—

it spattered over Mrs. Washington's beautiful purple silk costume.

Dolly gasped, "Oh, I'm so sorry! I've spoiled your lovely dress!" She wished she were anywhere but in this embarrassing spot!

"Do not worry, Mrs. Todd," said Mrs. Washington. "It is nothing at all."

Her gentleness made Dolly feel even more ashamed. Dolly knew that the beautiful silk gown was ruined. For the rest of her visit, she was miserable. Soon, she and Anna said thank you and good-by to their hostess and left.

As they walked home, Dolly felt that she had disgraced herself. And she was sure that she would never again be invited to the Washingtons'. "I shouldn't expect to mix with those society people," she told herself. "My place is with John and my baby in our own little home."

For three years she and John were very happy. They bought themselves a home.

The baby was just learning to walk and to talk when a yellow fever epidemic broke out in Philadelphia. Every day more and more people became ill. Every day more people died from the fever.

Dolly's second baby was born at the time the fever started.

"I can't let thee stay in the city," said John. "I shall take thee and the children to Gray's Ferry. It is cool out there. It is far away from the city. Thee will be safe."

"Stay with us out there," begged Dolly. "I want my husband to be safe, too."

John shook his head. "I must come back to take care of my father and mother."

He took Dolly and the children out to Gray's Ferry. Then he hurried back to the city. A few days later both his father and mother were dead.

Even then he couldn't go to Dolly. In some of his friends' homes everybody in the house was ill. There was nobody left to nurse them. John went from house to house. He did what he could to help them all.

At last cool weather came. The worst of the fever was over. John could go back now to his wife and children.

But he was worn out, and people who were weak and tired caught the fever easily.

Dolly's mother was taking care of Dolly and the babies out at Gray's Ferry. She hurried to the door when she saw John coming.

"John!" she cried. "Thee must be tired. Come in and lie down at once."

"Let me see Dolly first," begged John.

Dolly had heard him, too. She came running downstairs. She threw her arms around his neck.

"Don't leave me again," she cried.

That night John was taken with the fever. Dolly caught it from him. The baby caught it from Dolly.

Dolly was very ill. For days she was too weak to know what was happening. At last she began to grow stronger.

"Why doesn't John come to see me?" she asked. "And where is my baby?"

Then, at last, they told her. John and the baby had both died. Dolly and her little son Payne were left alone now.

Dolly Todd Becomes Dolly Madison

DOLLY MISSED John very, very much. She felt very lonely without him, but she knew it was foolish to keep on being sad. Her little boy needed a happy mother. Her mother needed a cheerful daughter. She must brighten up.

There were more men than women in this new country. Young widows were expected to marry again. Many of them did so very quickly. George Washington's wife had been the Widow Custis. Thomas Jefferson's wife had been a widow, too.

Dolly was still very young. She was very pretty. Nobody was surprised when the young men began to pay her attention again.

After Father had lost his money, Mother had begun to run a boardinghouse. It was a good boardinghouse, too. Some of the best-known men in Congress stayed at her house.

Of course Dolly helped her all she could. Dolly was good at helping. She knew how to make Mother's guests feel at home. She could get them talking at dinner. She could make them enjoy themselves.

"Thee is from New York, isn't thee?" she asked one of Mother's guests.

"That's right. And I believe you come from Virginia?"

"Indeed, I do."

"Some of the finest men in Congress come from Virginia. Look at James Madison."

"He isn't so much to look at," another of the guests said, laughing. "He is a sort of dried-apple little man."

"He's done as much for his country as any

other man in America. Have you ever met him, Mrs. Todd?"

"No," said Dolly, "but I believe I would like to. I have heard so much about him."

She didn't dream that James Madison would like to meet her. How could she know that he had seen her out walking with her little son? Or that he thought she was very pretty?

Mr. Aaron Burr knew, though. He was one of Mother's guests. He liked to tease Dolly. The next day he was chuckling when he came to dinner at the boardinghouse.

"Mistress Dolly, you must stop stealing the hearts of our bachelors in Congress."

"But I don't," Dolly said with a smile.

"But you do. James Madison said to me today, 'I want to talk with you about something important.' I thought he wanted me to vote for some new law. But that wasn't it. He wanted me to introduce him to you."

182

"I shall be glad to meet him," said Dolly. She said it very primly. Nobody could have told she was pleased, but she was.

As soon as dinner was over, she wrote a note to her best friend:

Dear Friend:

Thee must come to me. Aaron Burr says that the great little Madison has asked to be brought to see me this evening.

She chose her prettiest gown. It was of soft, mulberry-colored satin. She had a soft silk kerchief about her neck. She wore a little white cap. Her black curls just *would* peep out beneath the cap, no matter how hard she tried to pin them back in place.

Candles were lighted in the parlor. They shone against the dark-red mahogany table. Dolly and her friend waited. They heard the big knocker on the door. They heard the maid unbar the door. Then the two men were standing in the parlor. They were bowing low.

"Mrs. Todd, may I present Mr. James Madison?" said Aaron Burr.

Mr. Madison wore a black suit. There were ruffles on his shirt. There were silver buckles on his shoes. His hair was powdered.

"He isn't a dried-apple little man at all," thought Dolly. "I like him very, very much."

A WEDDING AT LUCY'S HOME

It was a bright September afternoon not many months later. Dolly's sister Lucy was very happy and excited.

She had been married now for several years. Today she was going to have company.

She had kept her servants busy the last week getting ready for that company. They had waxed

184

all the floors. They had polished all the candlesticks. They had swept and dusted every corner of her big, old-fashioned house.

"Miss Lucy acts as if she never had any company before," grumbled one of the girls.

"She never had company like this. 'Tisn't every day folks come here to get married."

"You mean we're going to have a wedding in this house?"

"Yes, ma'am. Miss Dolly is coming here to marry Mr. James Madison, right here in this room, day after tomorrow."

"My lands! I reckon I'd better give this-here brass andiron an extra rub, then!"

Just then Miss Lucy came hurrying down the steps. Far down the road, she could see a coach.

"Here comes Dolly!" she called.

Two days later, parlors were packed with friends. Outside, on the porch, the servants crowded around the windows to peep inside.

186

Dolly Payne Todd was being married to James Madison.

"She sure is a pretty bride," one of the servants whispered.

"Yes, ma'am. And she's sweet as she is pretty."

THE PRESIDENT'S WIFE

At first, Dolly Madison and her husband lived at his home in Virginia. Then, when Thomas Jefferson became President, he asked his friend James Madison to be his Secretary of State.

There was a brand-new city now on the banks of the Potomac River. It was named for George Washington. It was built expressly to be the capital of these new United States. There was a new house built for the President.

Thomas Jefferson's wife was dead. When he gave parties in his new house, he asked Dolly to be his hostess. After Jefferson, James Madison himself became President. The White House was Dolly's home, then, for eight long years.

How she enjoyed it! She gave many fine dinners for her husband's friends. She had teas and receptions and parties of every kind.

Now, at last, she could wear the beautiful clothes she had always longed for when she was a little girl. They were finer, even, than anything she had ever dreamed about. Could little girl Dolly ever have imagined herself in a dress of rose-colored satin, with a white velvet train two yards long? Could she have dreamed of a gold girdle with a gold necklace and bracelets? Could she have dreamed of ostrich tips in her hair, with a gold-embroidered crown? Yet she wore all these elegant clothes and jewels one night at a President's reception.

It wasn't because of her fine clothes and dinners and parties that everybody knew and loved Dolly. It was because she was still the same

Dolly Payne. She liked to help other people enjoy themselves and be comfortable.

THE PORTRAIT OF WASHINGTON

When Dolly made a promise, she kept it.

During the War of 1812 the enemy was very near Washington. Many people were leaving the city. Dolly was not afraid.

"I shall wait until my husband comes back," she said.

A very valuable painting of George Washington by Gilbert Stuart hung in her dining room.

"Do you suppose it is safe?" asked Mrs. Washington's grandson. "If the enemy should break through——"

"I'll take care of it," said Dolly.

Next day there was fighting so close that Dolly could hear the cannon. The American troops began to give way.

Soon the streets of Washington were filled with people rushing to get across the river before the enemy arrived.

"The Redcoats are coming! They will burn the town!" people cried.

At last two messengers came dashing up to the White House. They were covered with dust. They brought Dolly word from her husband: "We have lost. You must leave at once."

The day before, Dolly had packed her husband's most valuable government papers into trunks that would fill her carriage. There was no room for her own belongings. Now, as she hurried through the dining room, she could pick up only what little silver she could crowd into her handbag.

There still was George Washington's picture. She couldn't leave that. She had promised it would be taken care of.

It was a large painting. Its back was screwed

to the wall. It was hung so high one had to climb on a stepladder to reach it.

Dolly called to her servant. "Come, John, we must get the picture down."

There was no time to take it from its frame.

"Get your ax and break the frame," Dolly ordered him.

And, no matter how great the need for hurrying, she waited until the picture was carefully taken out, rolled up, and carried safely away. Then she was ready to join her friends.

The White House was burned. So was the Capitol. The fires lighted the sky so the red glare could be seen for miles. It was a ruined city to which Dolly returned a few days later.

Dolly was never one to fret over what she couldn't help. She found a new house. Soon she had made it into a home.

It was a very happy home when the news of peace came. Its doors stood open wide. It was

191

crowded with friends who had come to rejoice with Dolly and her husband. The servants joined in the gaiety, and later one of them wrote, "Such another joyful time was not seen in all Washington."

ONE OF THE BEST-LOVED WOMEN IN AMERICAN HISTORY

So Dolly became famous. The soldiers marching home stopped to cheer before her house.

It wasn't because of what she did. She was so busy taking care of people who were doing big and important things, she never had a chance to do them herself. She didn't expect people to think that *she* was wise or brave or smart. She was always just helpful and friendly. And that was enough.

It was enough to make Dolly Payne Madison one of the best-loved women in all of American history.

More About This Book

WHEN DOLLY MADISON LIVED

1768   DOLLY MADISON WAS BORN IN VIRGINIA, MAY 20.

The thirteen colonies were ruled by England.

The population of the colonies was about 2,660,000.

1775   DOLLY STARTED TO SCHOOL.

Patrick Henry made his famous "liberty or death" speech, 1775.

Paul Revere made his famous ride, 1775.

The first battle of the Revolutionary War was fought at Lexington, Massachusetts, 1775.

The Second Continental Congress met, 1775.

1776   DOLLY AND HER FAMILY MOVED TO SCOTCH-TOWN.

The Declaration of Independence was signed, 1776.

Thomas Paine wrote *Common Sense*, 1776.

The Battle of Long Island was fought, 1776.

General Burgoyne surrendered, 1777.

1781 THE PAYNE FAMILY MOVED TO PHILADELPHIA.
Cornwallis surrendered at Yorktown, 1781.

The peace treaty with England was signed, ending the Revolutionary War, 1783.

John Fitch experimented with steamboats, 1785.

The Constitutional Convention met to frame the United States Constitution, 1787.

The Northwest Territory was established, 1787.

1788 DOLLY MARRIED JOHN TODD.
George Washington was the first President, 1789-1797.

A banking system was established in the United States, 1791.

Captain Robert Gray discovered the Columbia River, 1792.

Eli Whitney invented the cotton gin, 1793.

1794 DOLLY MARRIED JAMES MADISON, SEPTEMBER 15.
John Adams was President, 1797-1801.

George Washington died, 1799.

Thomas Jefferson was President, 1801-1809.

The United States bought the Louisiana Territory from France, 1803.

Zebulon Pike explored the area now known as Kansas, Colorado, and New Mexico, 1806.

James Madison was President, 1809-1817.

The War of 1812 was fought, 1812-1815.

The "Star-Spangled Banner" was written, 1814.

American settlers reached Oregon, 1836.

Elias Howe invented the sewing machine, 1846.

1852   DOLLY MADISON DIED, JULY 12.
Millard Fillmore was President.

There were thirty-one states in the Union.

The population of the country was about 24,841,000.

DO YOU REMEMBER?

1. What present did Mr. and Mrs. Payne bring Walter and Temple?

2. Who was Dolly—or Dolley, as she sometimes spelled it—named for?

3. Who were the Knights of the Golden Horseshoe?

4. Why were the Payne house keys carried in a basket?

5. Why was Mr. Payne angry when he found Dolly dancing at the slave quarters?

6. How did Dolly learn the alphabet?

7. How did the Payne family escape the Tarleton raiders?

8. Why were the Payne family slaves freed?

9. What was Jack Jouett's brave deed?

10. Which one of the slaves refused to be freed?

11. How did the Payne family cross a wide, deep river on the way to Philadelphia?

12. How did people learn news events?

13. How were the new styles presented to the ladies?

14. What was Dolly's baby's name?

15. What happened when Dolly saw President Washington the first time?

16. Where were Dolly and James Madison married?

17. How long did Dolly live in the White House?

18. What famous portrait did Dolly save when the White House was burned in the War of 1812?

19. How was Dolly dressed for school?

20. Why did Grandmother put boards on the floor during candlemaking?

21. What did General Tarleton do at Scotchtown?

IT'S FUN TO LOOK UP THESE THINGS

1. Where are the Blue Mountains?
2. How do you play Grind the Bottle?
3. Find pictures of a Franklin stove.
4. Can you find a recipe for Philadelphia pepper pot?
5. Where did fireworks originate?
6. What is a kitchen-house?
7. What was a roasting kitchen and how was it used?

INTERESTING THINGS YOU CAN DO

1. Visit an antique shop. Notice old spinning wheels, pictures, candlesticks, iron kettles, trivets, high-boys, cradles.
2. Make a linen or butcher-linen sampler, size 10" x 12", and cross-stitch the alphabet on it. Or work a few flowers, a house or church, people or animals, and add your name.
3. Make a map showing the route taken when the Payne family moved from Hanover County, Virginia, to Philadelphia.
4. Make a layout of Scotchtown plantation.

5. Find pictures of the many different kinds of gourds. Show some of their uses for decoration.

6. Write a description of a Quaker church meeting and put on bulletin board.

OTHER BOOKS YOU MAY ENJOY READING

Abigail Adams: A Girl of Colonial Days, Jean Brown Wagoner. Trade and School Editions, Bobbs-Merrill.

Andy Jackson: Boy Soldier, Augusta Stevenson. Trade and School Editions, Bobbs-Merrill.

Dolly Madison, Jane Mayer. Trade Edition, Random House, School Edition, Hale.

Spy in Old Philadelphia, A, Anne Emery. Rand McNally.

Thomas Jefferson, Champion of the People, Clara Ingram Judson. Follet.

INTERESTING WORDS IN THIS BOOK

asparagus (ăs păr′à gŭs) : a plant used for food

baste (bāst) : to moisten roasting meat with melted butter or drippings

brocade (brŏ kād′) : a cloth with raised design in silk, silver, or gold

198

burdock (bûr′dŏk′) : a plant having burs for flower heads

chandelier (shăn dĕ lēr′) : light fixture, with several branches, hanging from the ceiling

choir (kwīr) : group of singers

clapboard (klăp′bōrd) : overlapping boards for outside walls of a house

complain (kŏm plān′) : grumble

curtsy (kûrt′sĭ) . bow, with one knee bent

drippings (drĭp′pĭngz) : fat and juices dripped from roasting meat

dungeon (dŭn′jŭn) : close, dark prison underground

fashionable (făsh′ŭn à b'l) : dressed in the latest style

finery (fīn′ēr ĭ) : fancy clothes or jewelry

forbidden (fŏr bĭd′dĕn) : banned

forgiving (fŏr gĭv′ĭng) : not holding anger

gaudy (gôd′ĭ) : flashy; showy

homesick (hōm′sĭk′) : longing for home

homespun (hōm′spŭn′) : coarse, plain cloth woven at home

honeysuckle (hŭn′ĭ sŭk′ 'l) : vine with sweet-smelling white, yellow, or red flowers

hostess (hōs′tĕs) : lady who entertains

introduce (ĭn′trô dūs′) : to make people acquainted with each other

invade (ĭn vād′) : to enter and attack

legislature (lĕj′ĭs lā′tŭr) : group of persons who make laws

mournful (mōrn′fŏol) : sad; full of sorrow

namesake (nām′sāk′) : a person named after another person

nightfall (nīt′fôl′) : close of the day; dusk

persimmon (pēr sĭm′ŭn) : tree, with plumlike fruit, sweet-tasting when ripe

pinafore (pĭn′à fōr′) : an apron, low-necked and sleeveless, usually worn by children

pine tags (pīn tăgs) : dried pine needles

quarters (slave) (kwôr′tērs) : group of cabins for plantation Negroes

spit (spĭt) : a rod for holding meat over a fire

spooky (spōōk′ĭ) : ghostly; scary

startled (stär′t′ld) : alarmed or frightened

strut (strŭt) : to walk with a proud gait or swagger

trinket (trĭng′ kĕt) : a small ornament, as a ring or pin